Key Stage 3 Mathematics
Numeracy Strategy Book 2

This book has been _written specifically_ to cover the Numeracy Strategy at levels 5-6.

Each page contains questions covering a topic of the Numeracy Strategy. Tips have also been included for some of the more difficult questions.

And there's even the odd ever-so-nearly entertaining bit, just to help keep you awake.

What CGP is all about

Our sole aim here at CGP is to produce the highest quality books — carefully written, immaculately presented and dangerously close to being funny.

Then we work our socks off to get them out to you — at the cheapest possible prices.

Contents

Contents

Section Five — Shape, Space and Measures

Section Six — Handling Data

Published by CGP

Contributors:

Charley Darbishire

Chris Dennett

Deborah Dobson

Kerry Kolbe

Simon Little

Andy Park

Glenn Rogers

Claire Thompson

James Paul Wallis

Chrissy Williams

With Thanks to:
Rebecca May and Katherine Reed for the proofreading.

ISBN: 978 1 84146 045 1

Groovy website: www.cgpbooks.co.uk

Printed by Elanders Ltd, Newcastle upon Tyne.

Based on the classic CGP style created by Richard Parsons.

Place Value and Ordering

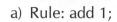

Q1 Write the next five numbers in each case:

a) Rule: add 1;   3, 4, __ , __ , __ , __ , __

b) Rule: add 0.1;   3.1, 3.2, __ , __ , __ , __ , __

c) Rule: add 0.01;   5.40, 5.41, __ , __ , __ , __ , __

d) Rule: add 0.01;   4.97, 4.98, __ , __ , __ , __ , __

e) Rule: subtract 0.1;   4.3, 4.2, __ , __ , __ , __ , __

f) Rule: subtract 0.02;   5.84, 5.82, __ , __ , __ , __ , __

Q2 Copy and complete these calculations:

a) $430 \times 0.1 = 430 \div \underline{} = \underline{}$

b) $673 \times \underline{} = 673 \div 100 = \underline{}$

c) $8137 \times \underline{} = 8137 \div 1000 = \underline{}$

d) $18\,430 \times 0.01 = \underline{} \div \underline{} = \underline{}$

e) $127 \times 0.1 = \underline{} \div \underline{} = \underline{}$

f) $8 \times 0.01 =$

g) $73 \times 0.001 =$

h) $2.3 \times 0.1 =$

> *multiplying by 0.1 is the same as <u>dividing by 10</u>*
> *multiplying by 0.01 is the same as <u>dividing by 100</u>*
> *multiplying by 0.001 is the same as <u>dividing by 1000</u>*
> *multiplying by 0.0001 is ... OK, I'm getting bored now.*
> *You get the idea...*

Q3 Write down:

a) The number 0.01 more than 7.72

b) The number 0.01 more than 7.89

c) The number 0.001 more than 0.654

d) The number 0.001 more than 0.649

e) The number 0.02 less than 1.41

f) The number 0.002 less than 9.943

g) The number 0.002 less than 6.280

h) The number 0.001 less than 10

Q4 In each case, find TWO numbers
— one to give an answer bigger than 5 and one to give an answer smaller than 5.

a) $5 \times ? =$

   $5 \times ? =$

b) $5 \div ? =$

   $5 \div ? =$

Rounding Numbers

Q1 Round each of these numbers to (i) 1 decimal place (ii) 2 decimal places:

a) 7.431   e) 1.191

b) 9.829   f) 2.299

c) 121.119   g) 9.991

d) 345.678   h) 4.999

> Look at the next digit _TO THE RIGHT_.
> If it's less than 5, _ROUND DOWN_. If it's 5 or more, _ROUND UP_.
> e.g. to round 5.4367 to 2 decimal places, look at the 3rd digit after
> the decimal point — which is 6, so _round up_ to get _5.44_.

Q2 Use your calculator to write these as decimal fractions. Use the "dot" notation if appropriate.

a) $\frac{1}{8}$ e) $\frac{7}{16}$

b) $\frac{1}{16}$ f) $\frac{7}{11}$

c) $\frac{1}{9}$ g) $\frac{1}{3}$

d) $\frac{5}{8}$ h) $\frac{5}{11}$

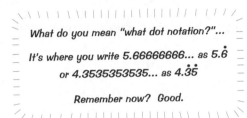

What do you mean "what dot notation?"...

It's where you write 5.66666666... as $5.\dot{6}$
or 4.3535353535... as $4.\dot{3}\dot{5}$

Remember now? Good.

Q3 In 2000 there were 2086 thousand hectares of wheat, 1128 thousand hectares of barley and 109 thousand hectares of oats growing in my back garden. (I have a big garden.)

a) Write each area out in words.   _(e.g. "Two million and eighty-six thousand hectares." Oops I've given you the first one... Well do the others!)_

b) Write the area of land growing wheat accurate to the nearest 10 thousand.

c) Write the area of land growing barley accurate to the nearest 10 thousand.

d) Write the area of land growing oats correct to the nearest 100 thousand.

Q4 19421 people went to Five's final concert. 5902 of these were 14-year-old girls. Surprisingly, 7494 of them were 63-year-old grannies named Ethel.

a) How many <u>people</u> went to the concert rounded to the <u>nearest 1000</u>?

b) How many <u>14-year-old girls</u> were there, rounded to the <u>nearest hundred</u>?

c) Round the number of <u>63-year-old grannies named Ethel</u> to the <u>nearest 10</u>.

d) Round the number of <u>63-year-old grannies named Ethel</u> to the nearest 100.

Ooo... J from Five is really fit...

Five have split up. Just get over it...

Yes and I'm afraid they're never coming back. But who could forget such classics as
Let's Dance, Everybody Get Up and Slam Dunk Da Funk... Anyway, the reason I'm mentioning
Five is because 5 is very important when you're rounding numbers. Make sure you know the rule
at the top of the page — the one that Fred is pointing to.

__Ordering and Integers__

Q1   Write each of these lists in ascending order:

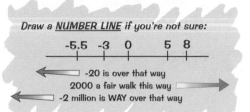

That means from the lowest to the highest.

  a) 6, -3, 8, -1, 1, -9

  b) 0, -3.3, 3.4, 0.4, -2.9, -0.5

  c) -213, -123, -132, -121, - 312, -231

  d) -0.101, 0.121, -0.123, 0.123, 0.312, -0.312

  e) 121.12, 121.21, 121.02, 121.01, 121.10, 120.21

  f) -74.4, -74.32, -79.39, -74.44, -74.404, -74.411

Draw a __NUMBER LINE__ if you're not sure:

-5.5 -3 0   5 8

← -20 is over that way
2000 a fair walk this way →
← -2 million is WAY over that way

Q2   Calculate the following:

  a) 2 – 7   e) 7 – - 6

  b) -6 – 8   f) -8 – -2

  c) 0 – 9   g) -3 – -3

  d) 5 – -2   h) 8 – 5 – - 3

Remember, two minus signs together make a plus

Q3   Complete this multiplication table:

×	2	-3	-5	7	8	-11
1	2		-5			
-4						
-5						
9					72	
-10						
6						

Stop nailing Daddy, Evil Kid.

Q4   Complete these number pyramids:

Each number is made by adding the two numbers underneath.

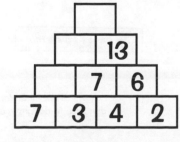

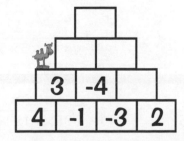

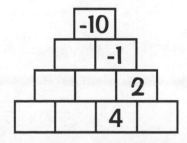

Prime Factors

Q1 List all the factors of the following numbers.

a) 12

b) 48

c) 81

d) 126

e) 200

f) 350

g) 27

h) 36

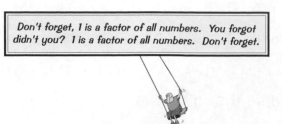

Don't forget, 1 is a factor of all numbers. You forgot didn't you? 1 is a factor of all numbers. Don't forget.

Q2 Find the prime factors of these numbers, and then write each number as a "product of prime factors":

a) 12

b) 48

c) 200

d) 350

Hint — use a factor tree like this:

Start by putting the number at the top.

Split it into factors like this. Circle any prime factors you get.

Keep splitting them into factors until you've only got prime ones.

Now you've got all the prime factors. Multiply them together to make the original number like this:

2 × 2 × 3 × 3 = 36

Q3 Use prime factors to find the <u>highest common factor</u> of the following pairs of numbers.

a) 18 and 24

b) 64 and 24

c) 120 and 65

d) 324 and 448

e) 495 and 4312

f) 75 and 77

Q4 Find the <u>lowest common multiple</u> of the following pairs.

a) 27 and 18

b) 99 and 165

c) 480 and 108

d) 324 and 448

e) 138 and 345

f) 265 and 371

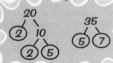

Use a tree to find the prime factors of each number. Then multiply all the factors together (but if a factor is in both trees, only count it once.)

Lowest common multiple is 2 × 2 × 5 × 7 = 140
(5 is in both trees, so we only count it once.)

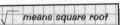

Q5 Write down:

NO CALCULATORS!!!!!
(for this question)

a) $\sqrt{3\times3}$

b) $\sqrt{5\times5}$

c) $\sqrt{2\times2\times5\times5}$

d) $\sqrt{3\times3\times5\times5}$

e) $\sqrt{5\times5\times7\times7}$

f) $\sqrt{35\times10\times14}$

$\sqrt{}$ *means square root*

Hint: Write as factors first — don't try to do long multiplication!

Squares, Cubes and Roots

Q1 Copy and complete (I did the first one for you):

    a) $10 \times 10 = 10^2 = 100 =$ one hundred

    b) $10 \times 10 \times 10 = 10^? = ? =$ one ?

    c) $10 \times 10 \times 10 \times 10 \times 10 = ? = ? = ?$

    d) $? = 10^7 = ? = ?$

    e) $? = 10^4 = ? = ?$

    f) $? = ? = ? =$ one million

Q2 Copy and complete (I helped again by doing the first one):

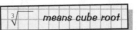

    a) $3^2 = 9$ therefore $\sqrt{9} = 3$ or -3

    b) $4^2 = ?$ therefore $\sqrt{?} = 4$ or -4

    c) $2^3 = ?$ therefore $\sqrt[3]{?} = 2$

    d) $? = 64$ therefore $\sqrt{64} =$

    e) $10^2 = 100$ therefore $? = ?$

> Square roots give _two answers_ — a positive and negative version of the _same number_.
> e.g. $\sqrt{16}$ is **4** or **-4**
>
> Cube roots only give _one answer_.
> e.g. $\sqrt[3]{8}$ is **2**
> $\sqrt[3]{-8}$ is **-2**
> A bit weird, I know. But hey, this is maths...

Q3 Show the approximate positions of these square and cube roots on a number line labelled from 0 to 10:

You can use your calculator for this question.

    a) $\sqrt{2}$ d) $\sqrt{60}$

    b) $\sqrt{30}$ e) $\sqrt[3]{30}$

    c) $\sqrt{50}$ f) $\sqrt[3]{900}$

Q4 Calculate these roots and powers. Give all answers correct to 3 d.p.

    a) 3.5^2 e) $\sqrt[3]{52}$

    b) 0.53^2 f) 10.1^3

    c) 7.3^3 g) $\sqrt{0.98}$

    d) $\sqrt{6.6}$ h) $\sqrt[3]{0.98}$

This one's a calculator question too.

Cube roots — well they're better than root canal surgery...

Putting little numbers above normal numbers may seem like a funny business for strange mathsy people. But if you actually know what it means, it makes more sense. 364^2 means 364×364. And 8^3 is $8 \times 8 \times 8$. "Square root of 50" means _the number which times by itself gives 50._ And "cube root of 50" means the number for which _number $\times$ number $\times$ number = 50._

Fractions

Q1 Draw 6 copies of this rectangle and shade:

a) $\frac{1}{2}$ c) $\frac{1}{6}$ e) $\frac{3}{8}$

b) $\frac{1}{3}$ d) $\frac{1}{8}$ f) $\frac{3}{4}$

Shade well you must, mmm?

Q2 Put these fractions in ascending order:

a) $\frac{1}{2}$ $\frac{3}{4}$ $1\frac{1}{4}$ $\frac{1}{4}$ $\frac{9}{2}$

b) $\frac{3}{4}$ $\frac{3}{8}$ $\frac{1}{4}$ $\frac{1}{8}$ $\frac{5}{8}$

c) $\frac{2}{7}$ $\frac{4}{7}$ $\frac{1}{7}$ $\frac{12}{7}$ $\frac{6}{7}$

d) $\frac{1}{2}$ $\frac{1}{4}$ $\frac{3}{8}$ $\frac{7}{16}$ $\frac{5}{8}$

e) $\frac{1}{5}$ $\frac{1}{10}$ $\frac{4}{20}$ $\frac{3}{5}$ $\frac{3}{10}$

f) $\frac{3}{20}$ $\frac{13}{50}$ $\frac{23}{100}$ $\frac{3}{10}$ $\frac{12}{25}$

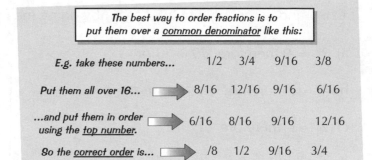

The best way to order fractions is to put them over a *common denominator* like this:

E.g. take these numbers...   1/2   3/4   9/16   3/8

Put them all over 16...   ➡   8/16   12/16   9/16   6/16

...and put them in order using the *top number*.   ➡   6/16   8/16   9/16   12/16

So the *correct order* is...   ➡   /8   1/2   9/16   3/4

Q3 Kerry keeps a collection of creepy crawlies. She has 10 beetles, 2 millipedes, 4 bluebottle flies, 3 spiders and a cricket.

a) What fraction of her collection is beetles?

b) What fraction is spiders?

c) What fraction is crickets?

d) What fraction is millipedes or flies?

e) Kerry gets peckish while doing her maths homework and eats 2/5 of her beetles. How many beetles are left?

f) She then collects 6 new beetles from the garden. What fraction of her collection is beetles now?

Q4 If Doris and Boris each have a half of a half of their tasty meat pizza, how much is left in the fridge? If Boris then eats 4/5 of the leftovers, what fraction of the original pizza is left for Chuck Norris?

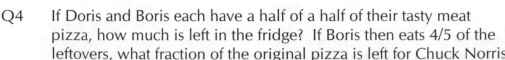
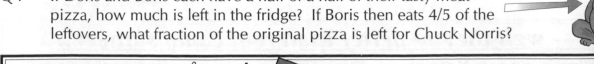

Hōnēṣṭĺŝ Ʋḥāṭ Ủûṣṭ İ C̣ ẹ̄ṭ ā ʌ̌řāč̣ṭĭō̄ ō̄ūṭ ō̄ʌ̂ ŝ̄ōūŭŭ̆ŭ̆

Y□□ □□□·□ □□□□□ □□□□□□□□□□□ □□□□□□□□□·□□ □□□□□□□□□□. İ□·□ □□□□□□□□ □□□□. **Y**□□ □□□□□ □□□□ □□□□ □□□□ □□□□□ □□□□□.

OUT OF ORDER

Section One — Numbers and the Number System

Fractions II

Q1 Work out these, giving your answers in their simplest form:

a) $\dfrac{5}{8}+\dfrac{1}{8}$ c) $\dfrac{2}{3}+\dfrac{1}{3}+1\dfrac{1}{3}$ e) $\dfrac{1}{8}+\dfrac{1}{2}$ g) $\dfrac{2}{3}+\dfrac{1}{7}$

b) $\dfrac{5}{7}+\dfrac{4}{7}$ d) $\dfrac{1}{2}+\dfrac{3}{4}$ f) $\dfrac{2}{3}-\dfrac{1}{6}$ h) $\dfrac{4}{5}-\dfrac{3}{4}$

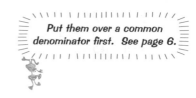

Put them over a common denominator first. See page 6.

Q2 Now these multiplications:

a) $\dfrac{1}{2}\times10$ c) $1\dfrac{1}{3}\times12$ e) $\dfrac{3}{2}\times\dfrac{3}{4}$ g) $\dfrac{6}{7}\times\dfrac{5}{9}$

b) $\dfrac{3}{4}\times32$ d) $\dfrac{1}{2}\times\dfrac{1}{4}$ f) $\dfrac{2}{3}\times\dfrac{5}{8}$ h) $1\dfrac{2}{3}\times\dfrac{6}{7}$

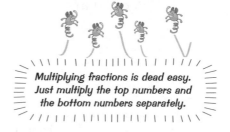

Multiplying fractions is dead easy. Just multiply the top numbers and the bottom numbers separately.

Q3 Now division!

a) $\dfrac{1}{2}\div4$ c) $\dfrac{1}{2}\div\dfrac{1}{2}$ e) $\dfrac{1}{2}\div\dfrac{1}{8}$ g) $2\dfrac{1}{5}\div\dfrac{3}{10}$

b) $\dfrac{1}{2}\div2$ d) $\dfrac{1}{2}\div\dfrac{1}{4}$ f) $\dfrac{1}{4}\div\dfrac{5}{8}$ h) $\dfrac{2}{7}\div\dfrac{8}{9}$

Q4 Pair up the equivalent fractions:

$3\dfrac{3}{4}$ $1\dfrac{1}{8}$ $\dfrac{15}{4}$ $1\dfrac{7}{20}$ $1\dfrac{1}{4}$ $\dfrac{27}{20}$

$\dfrac{23}{7}$ $\dfrac{42}{16}$ $3\dfrac{4}{14}$ $\dfrac{10}{8}$

$\dfrac{44}{8}$ $5\dfrac{1}{2}$ $\dfrac{27}{15}$ $\dfrac{9}{5}$ $2\dfrac{5}{8}$ $\dfrac{9}{8}$

Q5 Accident-prone Charley fell into a paper shredder. His remains were separated out. 3/8 of his remains was fleshy sludge. 1/3 was liquid. The rest was just powdered bone. What fraction of Charley was bone?

Come on, they're better than Dale Winton...

Ordering, adding and subtracting fractions is easy once you've learnt how to put fractions over a <u>common denominator</u>. And multiplying and dividing are dead easy too — you just need to learn the methods. So make sure you do <u>learn it all</u>. And just think, you may not like fractions, but Dale Winton could've been your dad, so never forget how lucky you are.

<u>Percentages</u>

Q1　Work out the following percentages.

a) 10% of 600

b) 5% of £45

c) 20% of £500

d) 15% of 60 m

e) 95% of 350 kg

f) 1% of 850 litres

g) 12.5% of 300 m

h) 16% of 678 kg

Q2　Complete this table:

percentage	decimal fraction	fraction
50	0.5	1/2
25		
20		
10		
5		
16		
36		
84		

Q3　Use the table above to write down the answers and three DIFFERENT ways to calculate these:

a) 50% of 568

b) 25% of 54

c) 20% of 4650

d) 10% of 67

e) 5% of 780

f) 16% of 375

g) 36% of 75

h) 84% of 75

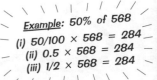

Example: 50% of 568
(i) 50/100 × 568 = 284
(ii) 0.5 × 568 = 284
(iii) 1/2 × 568 = 284

Q4　Is 34% of 68 the same as 68% of 34? Is 5% of 43 the same as 43% of 5? Will this always be true?

Proportion

Q1 1 gallon ≈ 4.5 litres (approx).

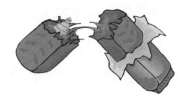

Weeeee...

a) How many litres are equivalent to 3 gallons?

b) How many litres are equivalent to 300 gallons?

c) How many gallons are equivalent to 1 litre? Write your answer as a fraction.

d) My car (pictured right) travels 52 miles on 1 gallon of petrol. How far would it go on 1 litre?

Q2 A box of 25 chocolate bugs bars (with real bug centre) at the cash-and-carry costs £4.75.

a) How much does one bar cost?

b) How much do 5 bars cost?

c) Samson makes a 4p profit on every bar he resells.
   Write his profit as a fraction of the cost of each bar.

Q3 Tim just loves his perfect smile. He buys 5 m of dental floss from Supercheesygrin Dental Floss Supplies for £8.

a) How much would 1 m of floss cost? (You pay by length.)

b) How much would 6 m cost?

c) How much could he buy with £10?

Q4 Former pop star H from Steps is selling signed Steps goodies at a local church fete.
To help with the calculations he makes this "ready reckoner". Copy and complete the table.

Amount bought	Steps CD singles	Steps CD albums	Steps T-Shirts	H plastic doll
1	25p			
2	50p			
3				
4		68p		
5			£1.10	
6				78p

I think that young lad H is a real dirtbag.

And reaching the end of another page of maths, I thought "this IS happiness"...

And that's what many pop stars think when they do maths too. (I know for a fact that after a gig, there's nothing that the members of Steps like more than doing a few sums to relax.) Anyway, just remember: proportion is a big word, but proportion questions are just about multiplying and dividing.

Ratio and Proportion

Q1   At a Will Young concert, there are 12 000 girls and 8000 boys.
Write the ratio of boys : girls in its simplest form.

Q2   At a Gareth Gates concert, the ratio of boys to girls is 3 : 5.
There are 15 boys. How many girls are there?

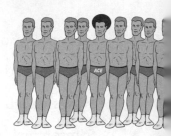

Q3   An army of 1000 clones has been created. However, an error in the
cloning process has given some of the clones afros and "Ace" pants.

a) If the ratio of normal clones to afro-ace-pants clones is 4 : 1,
how many normal clones are there?

b) What fraction of the clones have the afro-ace-pants defect?

Q4   Yesterday my cat, Smudge, dragged in 25 mice, 15 birds and 10 walruses from the garden.

a) Write the ratio of Smudge's kills in its simplest form.

b) What fraction of the animals were birds?

c) What fraction of the animals were not walruses?

Q5   To make compost, Uncle Urrgh uses 3 parts grass cuttings, 1 part
kitchen waste and 5 parts (used) toilet paper. If he wants to make
45 barrows of compost, how much of each ingredient does he need?

Q6   Measured on a map, the distance from Itchybaldhead Cottage to Itchybaldhead Forest is 7 cm.
If the true distance is 17.5 km:

a) What actual distance does 1 cm on the map represent?

b) Write the scale of the map as a ratio 1: something.

c) The local Parish of Itchybaldhead is 6 km from
Itchybaldhead Cottage. How far will this be on the map?

Q7   On a plan of Rushteloo farm, the outdoor loo is 60 cm from the back door. The scale of
the plan is given as 1 : 1500. How far will farmer Ted have to run when he needs the loo?

This one's for all you teachers out there... ***All we hear is Ratio Ga Ga, Ratio Goo Goo, Ratio Ga Ga...***

That's it — it's all over — no more maths — that's the end of... er, hang on a minute, Section One.
So the good news is that there are loads more scrummy pages of maths questions for you to enjoy.

Multiplying, Dividing and Inverses

Q1 Calculate these:

a) 7 × 4

b) 8 × -3

c) -9 × -4

d) -3 + -2 + -1

e) 3 − (4 + 5)

f) 3 + (4 − 5)

g) 3 − (2 − 4)

h) 7 − (3 × (4 − 2))

Q2 Use this fact to write down answers to the following:

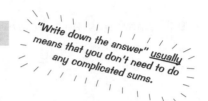

$$78 \times 561 = 43758$$

"Write down the answer" usually means that you don't need to do any complicated sums.

a) 43758 ÷ 561

b) 43758 ÷ 78

c) 7.8 × 561

d) 7.8 × 5.61

e) 43.758 ÷ 7.8

f) 437.58 ÷ 5.61

g) 43758 ÷ 156

h) 43758 ÷ 39

Hint: 78 × 2 = 156

Q3 Use estimation to check this homework. Correct any that are wrong.

a) 56 × 98 = 2488

b) 78 × 0.4 = 31.2

c) 18.6 ÷ 12 = 1.55

d) 6244 ÷ 4 = 5161

e) 4.1 − (7.8 − 12) = 8.3

f) $\dfrac{8 + 5.1}{2.3 + 2.2} = 2.91$ (to 2 d.p.)

g) $\dfrac{4.1 + 8.8}{3.2} = 6.85$

h) $\dfrac{7.4 \times 1.2}{4.8 - 1.6} = 0.25$

Q4 Work backwards to find the missing numbers.

a) ? ÷ 4 − 7 = 1

b) ? × 3 + 46 = 109

c) (? − 11) × 4 = 12

d) (? − 4) ÷ 2 = 16

Order of Operations

Q1   Edward Breadhead uses his calculator to do this calculation: $\dfrac{12}{4 \times 0.5}$

     a) He gets an answer of 1.5. Is this correct?

     b) What has he done wrong?

     c) Write down the keys he should use to get the correct answer.

     d) Can you get the correct answer using another set of keystrokes?

Q2   Now Edward tries the following calculation, and gets an answer of 1.538. Silly Edward.

$$\frac{140}{7+13}$$

     What should he do to get the correct answer now?

Q3   Use your calculator to work these out:
(i) writing down all the intermediate stages,
(ii) without writing down any intermediate stages.

     a) $0.7 + (1.8 + 3.4) - (1.4 + 0.7)$ f) $\dfrac{37 - (21 - 4)}{4 \times \text{-}5}$

     b) $8.2 - (4.1 + 1.6) - (0.7 - 3.7)$ g) $3 \times (4 - 2 \times (0.7 \times 0.5))$

     c) $23.7 - 2 \times (4.3 - 1.9)$ h) $\dfrac{2 \times 0.4^2 - 2 \times 0.2^2}{3.1 - 2.48}$

     d) $104 - 7 \times (3.2 - 11)$

     e) $\dfrac{4.8 + 7.2}{0.2 \times 0.4}$

> **Remember:**
> Use <u>BODMAS</u> to get the <u>order of operations</u> right:
> Brackets, pOwers, Division, Multiplication, Addition, Subtraction.
> First ⟶ Last

Q4   **Challenge** — by inserting as many brackets as you like,
see how many different answers you can get for the following:

     $1 \times 3 + 5 - 3 \times 2 + 6 =$ 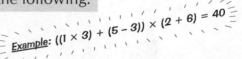

Example: $((1 \times 3) + (5 - 3)) \times (2 + 6) = 40$

I'd like a nose job and a triple heart-bypass please...

This all comes down to good old BODMAS. So remember — BODMAS BODMAS BODMAS BODMA...

Mental Methods

Q1   Copy these sums and fill in the gaps.

a) 37 + __ = 100   e) 1000 − __ = 670

b) 100 − 57 = __   f) 417 + __ = 1000

c) 10 − 3.6 = __   g) 0.43 + __ = 1

d) 8.3 + __ = 10   h) 0.871 + __ = 2

Q2   Work out the following. Percy the bird impressionist has offered to help.

a) 3×8 e) 20^2

b) 30×80 f) 200^2

c) 300×800 g) 4^3

d) 2^2 h) 40^3

Quack

Q3   Do these calculations **in your head**.

a) 19×4 e) 67×9

b) 19×8 f) 86×90

c) $224 \div 4$ g) $342 + 343$

d) $344 \div 8$ h) 670×99

Q4   The answers to the calculations in each group are the same.
Copy the sums and fill in the gaps **without** working out the answers.

a) 2×8 $0.2 \times ?$ $0.02 \times ?$ $? \times 0.8$

b) 4×13 $? \times 1.3$ $? \times 130$ $0.04 \times ?$

c) 0.7×1.1 $7 \times ?$ $11 \times ?$ $0.007 \times ?$

d) 127×0.07 $12.7 \times ?$ $7 \times ?$ $700 \times ?$

e) $12 \div 4$ $120 \div ?$ $1.2 \div ?$ $? \div 400$

f) $8.7 \div 12.1$ $87 \div ?$ $0.87 \div ?$ $? \div 0.121$

Mental Methods — Factors and Powers

Q1 Write down the following.

a) 2^3

b) 4^3

c) 3^2

d) $\sqrt{25}$

e) 5^3

f) $\sqrt[3]{27}$

g) $\sqrt[3]{1000}$

h) $\sqrt{64}$

Q2 Find the prime factors of these numbers.
Then write each of the numbers as a product of its prime factors.

a) 30

b) 18

c) 64

d) 39

e) 225

f) 98

g) 196

h) 385

Example: Prime factors of 24 are 2 and 3.
Then $24 = 2 \times 2 \times 2 \times 3 = 2^3 \times 3$

Q3 Do these WITHOUT a calculator.

a) $\sqrt{6^2 + 8^2}$

b) $\sqrt{5^2 + 12^2}$

c) $\sqrt{2^4 \times 3^2}$

d) $(4^2 - 3^2)^2$

e) $\sqrt[3]{2^3 + 19}$

f) $\left(3^2 + \sqrt[3]{64}\right)^2$

g) $\left(\sqrt{9}\right)^4$

h) $\left(\sqrt[3]{125}\right)^2$

Q4 Answer these questions:

a) How many seconds are there in 2 minutes?

b) How many seconds are there in 2 hours?

c) How many days are there in 5 weeks?

d) How many hours are there in 1 week?

e) If Rod's heart beats 60 times per minute, how many times does it beat from when he gets up at 7.30 am until he goes to bed at 10 pm?

Powers — the root of all evil...

To find **prime factors**, always **start** by **dividing by 2** till you get an **odd number**. Then if it ends in **5**, divide by **5**... if the digits add up to a multiple of **3** divide by **3**, etc. **Learn those tricks** and **use 'em**.

Mental Calculations

Q1 Do these calculations in your head.

a) 53 + 54

b) 330 + 350

c) 156 + 158

d) 3701 + 3801

e) 11 × 76

f) 34 × 9

g) 5.6 × 1.1

h) 73 × 39

Q2 Write each of these percentages as:
(i) a decimal fraction,
(ii) a fraction in its lowest terms.

a) 45%

b) 55%

c) 15%

d) 150%

e) 230%

f) 5%

g) 17.5%

h) 0.5%

Q3 Pair up the equal numbers from this blackboard.
The blackboard has a family of gorillas pointing at it.

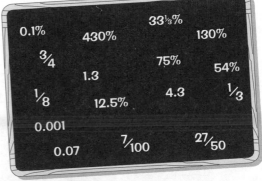

0.1%   430%   33⅓%   130%

¾   75%   54%

1.3

⅛   12.5%   4.3   ⅓

0.001

0.07   7/100   27/50

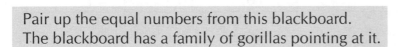

Q4 Find the mean of each of these sets of numbers without using a calculator.

a) 5   8   10   13   14

b) 15   18   20   23   24

c) 50   80   100   130   140

d) 71   73   74   74   78

e) 1023   1028   1030   1032   1037

f) 0.03   0.05   0.05   0.08   0.09

g) -12   -8   -6   -5   -4

h) -349   -351   -356   -344   -300

NO YAWNING

Word Problems and Puzzles

Q1   On a normal dice, the number of dots on opposite faces add up to 7.

a) If Lois rolls a dice and gets a 3, what will be
the score on the face that she cannot see?

b) If Lois rolls two dice and gets a 4 and a 1, what will be
the **total** score on the faces that she cannot see?

c) Copy and complete these two tables for the total scores on two dice. What do you notice?

Total of top faces		Score on Dice 2					
		1	2	3	4	5	6
Score on Dice 1	1	2		4		6	7
	2	3					
	3						
	4						
	5						
	6						

Total of bottom faces		Score on Dice 2					
		1	2	3	4	5	6
Score on Dice 1	1	12					7
	2	11					
	3						
	4					5	
	5						
	6						

Q2   Find 10% of 25% of 500.
Is it the same as 25% of 10% of 500?

Q3   Samson puts up the price of this wig by 10%.
What is the new price?
Afterwards, Delilah reduces everything in the shop by 10%.
How much is the wig then?

Q4   Using these cards as digits:

a) Make the largest possible number with the even
numbers on the cards.

b) Make the smallest possible number from all the
odd numbers on the cards.

c) Find the difference between these two numbers.

Q5   Find the product of the 2 consecutive odd numbers whose sum is 316.

Q6   Find the product of the 2 consecutive even numbers whose sum is -22.

Mental Methods — Estimation

Q1   Find approximate answers to these calculations. (Don't try to work them out exactly.)

a) 7.25 × 3.918

b) 87.8 ÷ 4.3

c) 43.8 + 107.9

d) 1070 − 983

e) $\dfrac{143 \times 57.2}{8.4}$

f) $\dfrac{27 \times 81}{0.31}$

Q2   The decimal point button on Desdemona's calculator is broken. Use estimation to insert the decimal point and/or zeros in the correct place for each of these calculations.

a) 4.34 × 6.7 = 29078

b) 11.7 × 470 = 54990

c) 93.1 × 3.3 = 30723

d) $\dfrac{4.1 \times 6.8}{43} = 64.837$

e) $\dfrac{74 + 138}{0.04} = 53$

f) 12 × (3.4² − 1.7²) = 10404

Q3   Delilah uses 500 g of meat to make a casserole for herself and Samson. How much meat should she buy if she is to cook for the 120 contestants in the World's Strongest Man competition?

Assume that Samson, Delilah and all the contestants eat the same amount.

Q4   Lois, a female gorilla, measures the gap for her new PC monitor as 33 cm wide and 39 cm high, correct to the nearest cm. At the 'Ape PC Universe' store there is a choice of monitors. Which should she buy to be certain that it will fit in the gap?

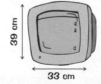
39 cm
33 cm

39 cm
32 cm

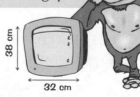
38 cm
32 cm

Q5   If a toilet cistern holds 2 gallons of water, estimate how many gallons of water your household flushes away each week. Use your estimate to work out how many gallons are flushed in your street, village or town.

Q6   Estimate how many bags of crisps your class eats in a week.

My estimate? — in about 5 mins I'll be going home...

Not only is estimating handy when your calculator's broken, it also gives you a rough idea whether your answers are in the right ballpark. You usually only need to round to 1 or 2 significant figures.

Written Methods — Multiplication

Q1   Using pencil and paper only, work out:

a) 31.8 + 42.7 + 83.8

b) 27.41 + 28.3 + 15.09

c) 2.31 + 23.1 + 231

d) 1046 + 164 + 0.146

e) 27 + 36 − 42 + 0.5

f) 234 − 34.2 + 4.23

g) 67.1 + 30.23 + 11.131 − 42.22

h) 0.012 + 0.314 + 0.505

Q2   Now use long multiplication for these.

a) 43 × 47

b) 242 × 65

c) 34.7 × 2.3

d) 4.3 × 12.5

e) 73 × 0.14

f) 57.1 × 0.23

g) 4300 × 1.23

h) 3.12 × 8.33

Q3   Work out 87 × 231. Then use your answer to work out the following.

a) 8.7 × 2.31

b) 87 × 23.1

c) 0.87 × 231

d) 870 × 2.31

e) 8.7 × 23.1

f) 870 × 0.231

g) 0.087 × 2310

h) 8.7 × 0.231

Q4   Write each calculation in the first column with the calculations in the other two columns which give the same answer.

3.1 × 4.7	31 × 47 ÷ 100	(3 × 0.47) + 0.047
9.9 × 63	21 × 463 ÷ 1000	(2 × 4.63) + 0.463
0.021 × 463	31 × 47 ÷ 1000	(2 × 4630) + 463
2.1 × 46.3	21 × 463 ÷ 100	(63 × 10) − (63 × 0.1)
31 × 0.047	21 × 463	(2 × 46.3) + 4.63
210 × 46.3	99 × 63 ÷ 10	(3 × 4.7) + (0.1 × 4.7)

Well quite...

Written Methods — Division

Q1   Work out the following, **without** using a calculator.

a) 357 ÷ 21

b) 744 ÷ 24

c) 676 ÷ 13

d) 437 ÷ 19

e) 231 ÷ 4.2

f) 27.6 ÷ 2.3

g) 8.84 ÷ 0.26

h) 0.923 ÷ 7.1

Q2   Give these answers as a whole number plus remainder.

a) 985 ÷ 4

b) 1000 ÷ 22

c) 345 ÷ 62

d) 999 ÷ 13

e) 812 ÷ 19

f) 234 ÷ 56

g) 568 ÷ 27

h) 77.5 ÷ 1.5

Q3   There are 426 Year 8 pupils at Smallville Secondary — and they are all going on a school trip. The transport company has buses with 64 seats, and coaches with 38 seats.

a) How many adults are needed if there has to be at least one adult for every 14 pupils?

b) How many seats are needed in total?

c) If the transport company is to use only coaches, how many should they send?

d) Instead the company sends 4 buses. How many people will these seat?

e) How many coaches will be needed for the rest?

f) How many empty seats will there be?

Q4   Divide £2700 in the ratio 1 : 5 : 8. Write your answers to the nearest penny. What do you notice about the total of your three answers?

Alas poor Yorrick — I knew him, O ratio...

Oh ho ho ho ho... Ahhh, written methods of multiplication and division — they're just one great big bundle of laughs, don't you think? It's all good practice, too — good wholesome fun all round.

Calculator Methods

Q1 Use the fraction button on your calculator to work out the following.
My friend Nadia is demonstrating the calculator fraction button for you.

a) $\dfrac{1}{8}+\dfrac{3}{7}$

d) $\dfrac{23}{25}+\dfrac{2}{7}$

g) $3\dfrac{3}{8}\times4\dfrac{1}{2}$

b) $\dfrac{4}{9}+\dfrac{1}{13}$

e) $\dfrac{1}{2}\div\dfrac{3}{8}$

h) $1\dfrac{1}{9}\div\dfrac{1}{3}$

c) $\dfrac{7}{9}+\dfrac{8}{11}$

f) $\dfrac{7}{8}\div1\dfrac{2}{3}$

Remember — to enter a __mixed__ fraction like $1\frac{3}{5}$ using the fraction button, you press: [1] [a⁰⁄c] [3] [a⁰⁄c] [5]

Q2 Use the fraction button to work out these 'time' problems.
Give your answer:
(i) as a fraction   (ii) as hours / minutes, or minutes / seconds.

Hint: Key in 1 minute and 20 seconds as $1\,^{20}\!/_{60}$.

a) 1 min 20 s + 5 min 47 s

b) 3 min 47 s + 2 min 32 s

c) 6 min 12 s + 4 min 4 s + 58 s

d) 3 h 12 min + 1 h 57 min

e) 2 h 47 min – 1 h 29 min

f) 8 h 12 min – 7 h 40 min

g) 3 × 2 h 49 min

h) 5 × 2 min 33 s

Q3 Convert these fractions to decimals.

a) $\dfrac{1}{2}$

b) $\dfrac{3}{4}$

c) $\dfrac{3}{8}$

d) $\dfrac{3}{16}$

e) $\dfrac{7}{16}$

f) $\dfrac{9}{250}$

g) $1\dfrac{3}{45}$

h) $7\dfrac{4}{29}$

Q4 Calculate these. Try not to be put off too much by the monkey — he's just trying to help.

a) $\dfrac{2\times3}{4+6}$

b) $\dfrac{4^{2}-3}{2}$

c) $\sqrt{8^{2}-3^{2}}$

d) $\sqrt{8\times2.3}$

e) $6\times\sqrt{1.44}$

f) $6(4+2^{2})$

g) $(6\times4+2)^{2}$

h) $6(4+2)^{2}$

Try and do these without writing down any intermediate steps.

Checking Results

Q1   Choose the correct answer to each calculation, **without** using a calculator.

a) 6.4 + 231.8   238.2   295.8   29.58

b) 7.3 × 11.8   19.1   861.4   86.14

c) 93.32 ÷ 105   1.289   0.289   0.889

d) $\sqrt{78}$ 39   2.8   8.83

e) $\sqrt[3]{5^2 \quad 3}$ 2.80   4.69   3.1

f) 6.1 × 23 ÷ 0.13   107.9   240   1079

Q2   Copy and complete these sentences.

a) The inverse of add is ....

b) The inverse of divide is ....

c) The inverse of multiply is ....

d) The inverse of subtract is ....

e) The inverse of square is ....

f) The inverse of halve is ....

g) The inverse of square root is ....

h) The inverse of cube is ....

Q3   Write a calculation you could do to check these answers.

a) 67.2 + 7.8 = 75   e) 9.4 × -7 = -65.8

b) 1.23 − 0.87 = 0.36   f) 3.2^2 = 10.24

c) 4 − 5 = -1   g) 6.1^3 = 226.981

d) 3.4 × 5.2 = 17.68   h) $\dfrac{8.4}{7.8}$ 1.077 to 3 d.p

Example: For part a), you could do 75 − 7.8 ... (and check the result is 67.2).

2 + 2 = 5? — yep, looks fine to me...

This is the bit everyone hates. Let's face it, once you've done the hard work and got an answer, the last thing you want to do is go back and do it again... but it's the only way you'll stamp out those silly mistakes. And don't even think of telling me you don't make them, I'm not listening... la de da...

Money, Percent and Ratio Problems

Q1 The original prices of selected items at two snooker shops are shown below. Both shops have sales on at the moment.

Come-on-Jimmy Snooker Supplies

Steve Davis's Electric Toenail Clipper £35

Ronnie O'Sullivan's Nostril Hair Remover £50

Stephen Hendry's Afro Wigs £40

Peter Ebdon's Hair Restoring Cream £25

John Higgins' Guide to Ice-Climbing £16

SALE SALE SALE SALE **20% OFF EVERYTHING** SALE SALE SALE SALE

Jimmy

SHOP A

Snookerplay Sports

Ronnie O'Sullivan's Nostril Hair Remover £50

Steve Davis's Electric Toenail Clipper £40

Stephen Hendry's Afro Wigs £40

Steve Davis's False Noses £5

Matthew Stevens' Anti-dandruff Shampoo £7.50

SALE!!! 30% off all items

Jimmy White Snooker

SHOP B

a) Work out the sale price of Peter Ebdon's Hair Restoring Cream in Shop A.

b) Work out the sale price of Ronnie O'Sullivan's Nostril Hair Remover in Shop B.

c) Keiron wants a Stephen Hendry Afro Wig and a Steve Davis Electric Toenail Clipper to help improve his game. Which shop should he go to?

Q2 The latest Clean Pants washing machine retails at £225. Alison has only £150 to spend. In a "mega sale", the discount starts at 5%, and increases by a further 5% every day. On what day of the sale will Alison be able to afford her dream machine?

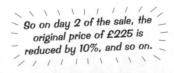

So on day **2** of the sale, the original price of £225 is reduced by 10%, and so on.

..yes, I just love my new washing machine. By the way, has anyone seen Smudge?

Q3 Glenda the Witch was killed when she accidentally turned herself into a dead toad. Her three remaining sisters are sharing out the contents of her cauldron in the ratio of their ages. Their ages are Heather 150, Claire 225 and Chrissy 375.

a) Write the ratio of their ages in its simplest form.

b) How many of each item do they get?

c) Claire doesn't like Vorbie Villiams so she divides her share equally between Heather and Chrissy. How many Vorbie Villiams CDs do they each have now?

Contents of Glenda's Cauldron:

20 newt eyes

10 worms

30 bat wings

Vorbie Villiams

Sving Vile you're Veennen

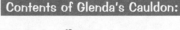

20 CDs of German pop star Vorbie Villiams

Number and Algebra Problems

Q1   Write three fractions that lie between $\frac{1}{2}$ and $\frac{3}{4}$.

Q2   Find:

   a) Two consecutive numbers that add up to 535.

   b) Two consecutive numbers that have a product of 756.

   c) Three consecutive numbers that add to 174.

   d) Four consecutive even numbers that sum to 404.

   e) Can you find two consecutive numbers that add to an even answer? Explain your answer.

   f) What about three consecutive numbers?

Q3   What is the last digit of 8^{11}?

Q4   A rectangle has sides $2x$ and $x + 3$, and a perimeter of 48 cm. What is its area?

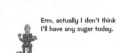

Q5   An extra-large sugar cube (pictured) has surface area 294 m^2.
      What is its volume?

Erm, actually I don't think
I'll have any sugar today.

Q6   For each sequence write down the next two terms,
      the 20th term and an expression for the nth term.

   a) 3   5   7   9   c) 54   49   44   39

   b) 24   31   38   45   d) -10   -8   -6   -4

Q7   Sam has 10 cans of worms and 15 single worms. Pratheeban has
      12 cans but has eaten 11 from one can. Every can contains x worms.

   a) Write expressions for the total number of worms that Sam and Pratheeban each have.

   b) If Sam and Pratheeban have the same number of worms, what is the value of x?

You'll worm to these questions eventually...

This is all about taking sentences in English and turning them into equations.
It's not easy — you've just got to keep practising 'em.

Shape and Space Problems

Q1   Juliet is blindfolded. Complete Romeo's instructions to guide her to him without getting hurt.

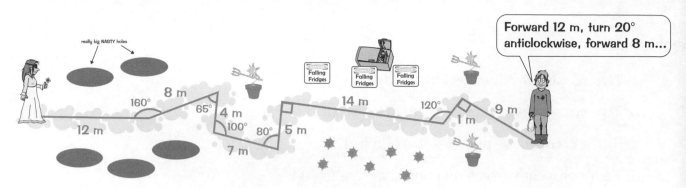

Q2   How can you slice through a square-based pyramid to give a new face that is:

a) a square?

b) a triangle?

c) a kite?

d) a trapezium?

Hint: draw some sketches.

A square-based pyramid is like an Egyptian one.

What shapes can you make by slicing a cone? List as many as you can.

Q3   Plot the points A(3, 0), B(0, -3) and C(-3, 0).

a) What are the coordinates of D if ABCD is a square?

b) Plot E if ABCE is a kite with the length of one diagonal = 9 units.

c) Plot F if ABCF is a trapezium, with CF parallel to AB and CF = 2 × AB.

d) Plot G if ABCG is a trapezium, with CB parallel to AG and CB = 2 × AG.

Q4   How many cubes with a volume of 8 cm³ can you
pack in a box measuring 12 cm × 8 cm × 16 cm?

Q5   Paul and Ali are on the road to Hell.

a) How many miles from Junction 7 to Junction 10?

b) How many miles from Junction 5 to Junction 8?

c) How many miles from Junction 8 to Junction 3?

M666 North Jct 6

M666 North
Hell   35
Jct 7   5
Jct 8   6
Jct 9   19
Jct 10   29

M666 South
Jct 5   2
Jct 4   10
Jct 3   14

Probability Problems

Q1 In a game at the village fête, players throw a dice. If they get an even number they win £2. If they get an odd number they lose the score showing on the dice (in £).

a) Make a table to show the possible winnings.

b) In 60 goes how many of each score are most likely?

c) What are the most likely winnings after 60 goes?

d) Is this a good money-making game for the fête?

e) One of the organisers proposes that the winning prizes should be increased to £3 each. Do you agree with her?

Q2 Rosamund has two bags of small monkeys and elephants. She picks animals at random from each bag.

Apparently, this question was written by Roger Carlsberg... strange that.

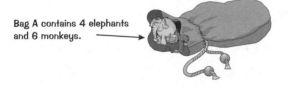

Bag A contains 4 elephants and 6 monkeys.

Bag B contains 5 elephants and 2 monkeys.

a) What is the probability that she gets an elephant when she picks from bag A?

b) What is the probability that she gets an elephant when she picks from bag B?

c) She picks an elephant from bag A and puts it in bag B.
   What is the probability of getting a monkey from bag B now?

d) What is the new probability of getting an elephant from bag A?

Q3 Tybalt has these cards. He chooses from them at random to make a three-digit number. Write down all the different numbers he could make.

a) What is the probability that he gets a number between 100 and 200?

b) What is the probability that he gets a number greater than 300?

c) What is the probability that he gets a multiple of 6?

d) What is the probability that he gets an even number?

e) What is the probability that he gets a number that is divisible by 9?

Carlsberg's — probably the best probability question in the world...

Remember, probability is all about <u>outcomes</u> — the number of successful outcomes compared with the total number of outcomes. By the way, always write down those two numbers before you do any calculating — it'll be much easier to check what you've done.

Problems on Data Handling

Q1   This graph shows the cost of sending a parcel with Crazy Couriers.

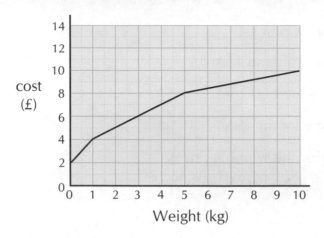

a) How much does it cost to send a parcel weighing 4 kg?

b) How much to send a parcel weighing 8.5 kg?

c) If a parcel costs £6.50 to send, how much does it weigh?

d) How much does a parcel weighing nothing cost to send? Explain what this means.

Q2   At a magic convention a survey is done on favourite spells.

Spell	witches' frequency	wizards' frequency
shrinking	10	11
gold-making	40	45
turn person to stone	15	7
automatic nose-picking	25	53
turn person into Hugh Grant	30	24

I say, you wouldn't mind awfully turning me back, would you?

a) Use the table to draw a pie chart of the witches' favourite spells.

b) Draw a compound bar chart showing the favourite spells of all the delegates.

c) What percentage of wizards favoured the "turn person into Hugh Grant" spell?

Oh that Mr Data Handling — he's such a joker...

Loads of practice with graphs — that's what you want, isn't it. Loads of lovely practice. Yup.
And here it is. Loads and loads and loads of practice. Smashing.

More Problems

Q1   Titania is trimming her nostril hairs. She finds a hair
which she measures as 63 cm to the nearest centimetre.

a) What is the longest length this hair could be?

b) How short could it be (and still measure 63 cm to the nearest cm)?

She trims the hair by 12 cm, again correct to the nearest cm.

c) What's the longest the piece she cuts off could be?

d) And the shortest?

e) Using your answers, calculate the longest and
shortest possible lengths of the remaining hair.

Q2

Beckpork scores winning goal for England!!!

Danny cuts out a picture of his favourite footballer, David Beckpork,
from a newspaper. It measures 8 cm × 8 cm to the nearest cm.

a) Work out the smallest area the square could be.

b) Work out the difference between
the largest and smallest possible areas.

Q3   Copy and complete this table.

Pattern No	Sum	Total
1	2	2
2	2 + 4	6
3	2 + 4 + 6	12
4	2 + 4 + 6 + 8	20
5	2 + 4 + 6 + 8 + 10	
6		
7		
10		
n		

*Hint: the total is related to the pattern
number. If you can't see it then try
drawing each total as a pattern of dots.*

Q4   Repeat question 3 but add odd numbers instead.

If you're really stuck, ask someone who nose how to do it...

This always gets me — measurements 'to the nearest whatever'. If someone told me that last night
I drank 20 pints (to the nearest pint), I wouldn't know whether I'd had 19½, 20 or 20½. Nightmare.

Puzzles and Investigations

Q1   Solve these mathematical puzzles.

a) Find the missing digits.

$$1\blacksquare^2 = \blacksquare\blacksquare4$$

there's two possible answers

b) Find the missing digits.

 ^{3} = ▢▢▢ 6

c) What digits do you NEVER get at the end of a square number?

d) What about at the end of a cube number?

e) What digit does 99^{11} end in?

Q2   The Daily Panic newspaper is made up of 10 (folded) sheets of paper.

a) How many pages will it have?

b) Decide which pages are printed on which sheet.

Back page   *Front page*

The Twelve Days of World Cup by Victoria B.
On the 1ˢᵗ day of the World Cup, David gave to me Alan Partridge in a pear tree.
On the 2ⁿᵈ day of the World Cup, David gave to me 2 tall Danes and Alan Partridge in a pear tree.
On the 3ʳᵈ day of the World Cup, David gave to me 3 French defenders, 2 tall Danes, ...
On the 4ᵗʰ day of the World Cup.... 4 crying Argies, 3 French defenders, ...
On the 5ᵗʰ day of the World Cup.... 5 golden balls, ...
On the 6ᵗʰ day of the World Cup.... 6 Gazzas crying, ...
On the 7ᵗʰ day of the World Cup.... 7 Svens a svinging, ...
On the 8ᵗʰ day of the World Cup.... 8 streakers streaking, ...
On the 9ᵗʰ day of the World Cup.... 9 Germans diving, ...
On the 10ᵗʰ day of the World Cup.... 10 Hansens humming, ...
On the 11ᵗʰ day of the World Cup.... 11 Linekers leaping, ...
On the 12ᵗʰ day of the World Cup.... 12 refs a blowing, ...

Q3   Victoria has written a song called "The Twelve Days of World Cup".

a) How many gifts arrive on the twelfth day?

b) How many gifts has Victoria received in total after the 12 days

c) Which items are there 36 of by day 12?

Puzzles and Investigations

Q1   Dermid says, "The sum of any two consecutive numbers is odd."

a) Use algebra to show why he's right.

b) Extend your reasoning to three and four consecutive numbers.

c) The sum of five consecutive numbers is always divisible by 5. Why?

d) Can you find any other similar sets of numbers?

Q2   Leanne is making boxes out of 20 cm × 20 cm pieces of card
(as shown). The lengths of all sides have to be whole numbers.

a) What are the dimensions of the box
with the biggest possible volume?

b) What are the dimensions of the box
with the smallest possible volume?

c) Has the box with the biggest volume
also got the biggest surface area?

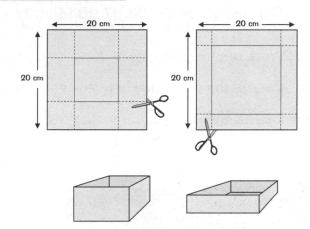

Q3   Popeye sells olives for 10% more than Brutus
BUT he sells 10% fewer. Who takes more money?

Q4   Here is a recipe for 10 stink bombs.

a) Adapt the recipe to make 50 bombs,
giving your answers in pounds and ounces.

b) Adapt the recipe to make 8 stink bombs.

c) Convert the recipe to metric units.

Stink bombs

8 oz mouldy potatoes

1 lb slimy cabbage

5 rotten eggs

6 oz gorgonzola cheese

Puzzled? Well here's a tip that won't help you at all...
Jabber, jabber, wibble, quack. Pass me the biscuit tin, Harold — I'm not sure that fish suits you.

Puzzles and Investigations

Q1   Draw a 10 x 10 number square like this:

1	2	3	4	5	6	7	8	9	10
11	12	13	14	15	16	17	18	19	20
21	22	23	24	25	26	27	28	29	30
31	32	33	34	35	36	37	38	39	40
41	42	43	44	45	46	47	48	49	50
51	52	53	54	55	56	57	58	59	60
61	62	63	64	65	66	67	68	69	70
71	72	73	74	75	76	77	78	79	80
81	82	83	84	85	86	87	88	89	90
91	92	93	94	95	96	97	98	99	100

Aha, here's the bug that frightened Mrs Reed. It's a nasty one, too...

a) Work out the products of opposite corners of the coloured rectangle.

i.e. work out 23 × 35 and 33 × 25.

b) What is the difference between your answers?

c) Investigate other similar rectangles.

i.e. do the same thing for other 3 by 2 rectangles in the number square and see what differences you get.

d) What happens to your answer if your rectangle is rotated through 90°?

e) Extend your investigation to other size number squares.

Q2   Can you slice a cube to give a new face that is:

a) a square?

b) an equilateral triangle?

c) a rectangle?

d) a parallelogram?

e) a regular hexagon?

f) an irregular hexagon?

A CUBE

If you ever see one of those bugs, my advice is RUN YOUR PANTS OFF...

This slicing up 3D shapes is a tricky business. It'd be fine if you could actually try it out with plasticine, but that always changes shape when you try and cut it. Hmm... yes, I've got it. Melon. Make some melon cubes and try cutting them up. Then you'll have a tasty treat for afterwards.

Algebra — The Basics

Q1   Simplify these expressions.

a) $h + h + h + h$

b) $g + g - g$

c) $3 \times f$

d) $4 \times e \times 2$

e) $d \times 2 \times c$

f) $(c + b) \times 5$

g) $b \times 7 - 4 \times b$

h) $5 \dfrac{a}{z}$

Q2   Write an equation to describe these.

a) The cost C (pence) of buying x Venus Bars at 24p each.

b) The cost C (pence) of buying 23 Venus Bars at k pence each.

c) The cost C (pence) of buying x Venus Bars at k pence each.

d) The cost C (£) of buying x Venus Bars at k pence each.

e) The number of sweets (N) each gets when 24 sweets are shared between 6 children.

f) The number of sweets (N) each gets when 24 sweets are shared between p children.

g) The number of sweets (N) each gets when q sweets are shared between 6 children.

h) The number of sweets (N) each gets when q sweets are shared between p children.

Q3   Draw lines to match each expression on the left with an equal expression on the right.

$p + p$	$2p$
$a - b + a$	0
$r + s - r$	$2v - 3$
$(t + t) \div 4u$	s
$v + 2 + v - 5$	$\dfrac{t}{2u}$
$a \times b$	$2a - b$
$\dfrac{1}{2} \times w \times x$	$\dfrac{wx}{2}$
$3 + y - 7 - y + 4$	ba

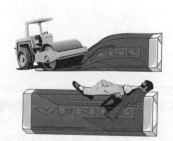

Algebra — Index Laws

Q1   If $a = 5$, $b = 3$ and $c = 1$, work out the values of each expression in these pairs.

a) $3a + b$ and $3(a + b)$

b) $2b - 2c$ and $2(b - 2c)$

c) $a + b/2$ and $(a + b)/2$

d) $a - b - c$ and $a - (b - c)$

e) $a^2 + c^2$ and $(a + c)^2$

f) $2a - b^2$ and $(2a - b)^2$

g) $12 - 3b$ and $(12 - 3)b$

h) $10a - 9b + 8c$ and $10a - (9b + 8c)$

Q2   Simplify:

a) $a \times a$

b) $b \times b \times b$

c) $c \times c \times c \times c$

d) $a \times b \times a$

e) $d \times f \times f \times d$

f) $g^2 \times g^2$

g) $hg \times hg$

h) $k^3 \times k$

Q3   These are more tricky. Simplify:

a) $z^2 \div z$

b) $y^4 \div y$

c) $x^7 \div x^3$

d) $4k^2 \div 2k$

e) $20m^4 \div 4m^3$

f) $0.5n^7 \div 0.25n^2$

g) $p \div p$

h) $q^3 \div q^3$

Q4   Really devious now. Simplify:

a) $a^4 \times a^2 \div a^3$

b) $b^2c \times bc$

c) $2de \times de^2$

d) $(3f)^2$

e) $(5g)^3$

f) $hj \times h^2j \div j^2$

g) $2km \times k \div m$

h) $6km \div m + 4k$

Maths — better than a bag of ants...

The best way to do the harder ones is one step at a time. Look at Q4 g). One step at a time means: *take the 2km, then multiply by k and write the answer down, then divide by m. Easy.*

Inverse Operations

Q1   In each case write two other equations that must also be true.

a) $8.1 - 3.7 = 4.4$

b) $7.1 + 9.8 = 16.9$

c) $a + b = 5$

d) $c - d = k$

e) $e + f = h$

f) $3e + f = h$

g) $7k - 4m = n$

h) $p^2 + q = r$

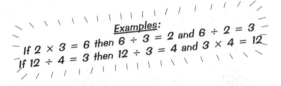

Example:
If $11 - 6 = 5$
then $11 - 5 = 6$
and $5 + 6 = 11$

Q2   In each case write two other equations that must also be true.

a) $5.1 \times 3.7 = 18.87$

b) $13.8 \div 6 = 2.3$

c) $ab = 6$

d) $hj = k$

e) $\dfrac{m}{n} = 4$

f) $pq = r$

g) $\dfrac{xy}{z} = a$

h) $b(c + 4) = d$

Examples:
If $2 \times 3 = 6$ then $6 \div 3 = 2$ and $6 \div 2 = 3$
If $12 \div 4 = 3$ then $12 \div 3 = 4$ and $3 \times 4 = 12$

Q3   Write the inverse of these operations.

a) $C = 3m$

b) $D = n + 1$

c) $E = p - 7$

d) $F = \dfrac{q}{6}$

e) $G = 2r + 1$

f) $H = 3s - 2$

g) $J = 2t + 7$

h) $K = u + 21$

Example:
If $A = k + 1$ then $k = A - 1$

Inverse Operations — not hard when you know what to do...

It's pretty much just a question of rearranging the equations. But don't try to do them in your head — write them down properly step by step. It's all too easy to make a silly mistake. Be warned.

Simplifying and Brackets

Q1 Simplify these expressions.

a) $3z + 2y - z$

b) $5a - 3a + 6a$

c) $4w + 2v - 4v + 2w$

d) $5c - 3d - 2d$

e) $3 + t + 2u - 3t + 7$

f) $f - 7 + 3f - 2g + 8$

g) $3s + 2r - 7 + 3r - 7s + 4$

h) $3 - 2h - 3j + h - 4$

Q2 Expand and simplify these expressions.

a) $p + 2(p + q)$

b) $2(r + 2s) + 3s$

c) $5t + 2(u + t) - 3u$

d) $3(v + 2w - x) - 4x + w$

e) $2(a + 2b) + 3(2a + c)$

f) $2(c - d) - 2(3c + d)$

g) $3 + 6(e + 4)$

h) $1 - (f - 2)$

Q3 Write an expression for the perimeter P of each shape.

a)

b)

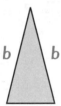

c)

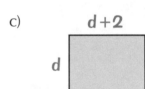

d)

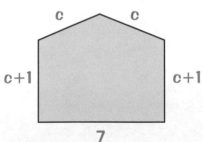

e)

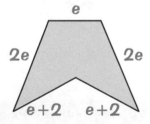

Q4 Build these expressions. One has been done for you.

Sequence: a plus b,   times 3,   divide by c,   subtract d

Expression: $a + b \rightarrow 3(a + b) \rightarrow \dfrac{3(a + b)}{c} \rightarrow \dfrac{3(a + b)}{c} - d$

a) e times f, add 4, times by 8

b) h plus j, square answer, subtract k

c) m times 2, subtract n, times by p, add q

Algebraic Relationships

Q1 Which of these are equivalent expressions?
Copy out the expressions, then draw lines to match each expression in the centre with its equivalent on the left, then its equivalent on the right.

$2(a + b)$	$3a + 4b + 6(b + 1) - 2a - 1$	$a + 5(2b + 1)$
$6a + 2b$	$0.5(12a + 4b)$	$4a - (2a - 2b)$
$a + 10b + 5$	$3(2 - a) + 4(b + 1) - 3$	$2(4 + 2b) + 5 - 3(a + 2)$
$7 - 3a + 4b$	$2a + 2b$	$2(b + 3) - 6(1 - a)$

Q2 Which of these shapes have the same area?

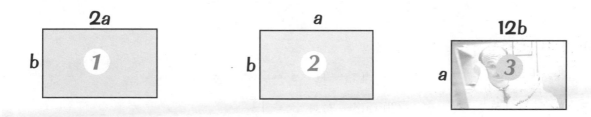

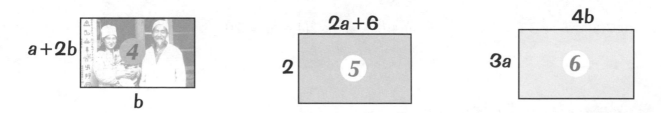

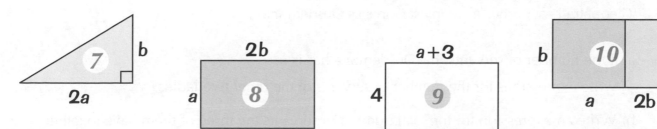

What do mathematicians eat for breakfast — 3x...

Have you seen that man's beady eye watching you? Question 2, number 3... And he's got a moustache, and he's bald... And he's only got half a face. Wasn't he a bad guy in an Arnie film?

Forming and Solving Equations

Q1   Solve these equations.

a) $z + 4 = 8$

b) $y - 8 = 3$

c) $2x = 8$

d) $3w = 15$

e) $\dfrac{v}{2} = 6$

f) $\dfrac{u}{12} = 3$

g) $5t = 8$

h) $8t = 5$

Q2   Solve these:

a) $2s + 1 = 5$

b) $3r - 5 = 4$

c) $(q + 1)/4 = 5$

d) $(p - 7)/3 = 7$

e) $11n - 9 = 13$

f) $m/3 + 2 = 6$

g) $5 - 2k = 1$

h) $12 - 0.5j = 9$

Pyramids were built to house the burial chambers of royalty

Q3   Now solve these:

a) $2(a + 1) = 10$

b) $3(b - 4) = 15$

c) $3(2c - 4) = 0$

d) $7(5 - d) = 35$

e) $2(e + 1) - 3 = 7$

f) $5(3 - f) + 3 = 13$

g) $4(g + 2) + 3g = 15$

h) $4(h + 2) + 2(4 - h) = 20$

Q4   Delilah has 4 more servants than Desdemona.
Cleopatra has 3 times as many servants as Desdemona.

a) If the number of servants that Desdemona has is k,

   write expressions for the number of servants of the other two ladies.

b) Write an expression for the total number of servants the three of them have together.

c) If there are 229 slaves altogether, form an equation.

d) Solve your equation to find out how many servants they each have.

Alternative Ways of Solving Equations

Q1 Solve each of these equations.

a) $5(z - 1) = 15$

b) $2(y + 7) = 22$

c) $4(5 - x) = 16$

d) $5(1 + v) = 35$

e) $4(u - 5) = 36$

f) $2(3 - t) = 6$

g) $4(s + 1) = 10$

h) $6(4 - q) = 30$

Ever felt out of place?

Q2 Which of these equations are equivalent?

Hint: You shouldn't NEED to work out the solutions to do this!

A: $x + 7 = 10$

B: $8 - x = 2$

C: $3x + 5 = 8$

D: $2x + 14 = 20$

E: $2 + 3x = 5$

F: $3x - 4 = 0$

G: $6x = 8$

H: $10 - x = 4$

Q3 Solve these equations and then write down which pairs of variables are equal.

a) $2a + 1 = 9$

b) $3b - 7 = 8$

c) $6c - 9 = 9$

d) $5(6 - d) = 5$

e) $\frac{1}{2}(e - 4) = 2$

f) $2f + 5 = 21$

g) $3(g + 1) = 15$

h) $2(h + 5) - 4 = 12$

Open wide.

More Complicated Equations

Q1　Solve these equations.

a) $3a + 1 = a + 7$

b) $2b - 7 = b - 3$

c) $3c - 2 = 2c + 4$

d) $10a + 1 = 8a + 9$

e) $b + 3 = 3b + 1$

f) $c - 1 = 2c - 8$

g) $3a + 1 = 5a - 3$

h) $4b + 4 = 7b - 5$

Q2　Jane has 3 identical bunches of bananas (each containing x bananas) and 2 single bananas. Tarzan has 1 bunch like Jane's, and 16 single bananas.

a) Write an expression for the number of bananas that each has in terms of x.

b) If they both have the same number of bananas, form an equation in x.

c) Solve your equation to find how many bananas in a bunch and how many they have each.

Q3　Desdemona has 3 times as many figs as Portia.
Desdemona gives 10 to Portia and then they have equal numbers.

a) If Portia had a figs to start with, write an expression for the number of figs each has now.

b) Form an equation in a, and solve it to find how many figs Desdemona had to start with.

Q4　Hamlet has 3 multipacks of Kat-Kit biscuits and 2 single biscuits. Othello has the **same total number** of biscuits but only has 2 multipacks and 8 single biscuits.

a) If there are y Kat-Kits in a multipack, write down an equation in y relating the number of biscuits Hamlet and Othello have.

b) Solve your equation to find how many Kat-Kit bars in a multipack.

More complicated — I thought they were hard enough already...

Equations like Q1 aren't really harder than normal — there are more steps, and so it takes longer, but each step is just as 'easy' as before. Start by getting all the letter bits (3a, 2c etc.) on *one* side.

Graphs and Proportion

Q1   Here are two currency conversion graphs.

a) How many euros do you get for £100?

b) How many euros do you get for £1?

c) Write an equation relating euros (e) to £ (p).

d) How many £ do you get for 50 euros?

e) How many $ do you get for £100?

f) How many $ do you get for £1?

g) Write an equation relating $ (d) to £ (p).

h) How many £ do you get for $50?

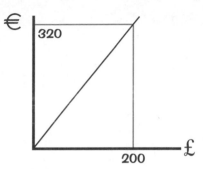

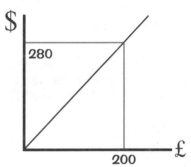

Q2   a) Sound travels at 330 m/s. Copy and complete the table.

time (s)	1	2	3	4	6	8
distance travelled (m)	330					

b) Write an equation relating time (*t*) and distance (*d*).

c) Use your table to draw a graph of distance against time for these figures.
Put time on the horizontal axis.

d) Use your graph to find how far away
the thunderstorm is if you count 6.5 seconds
between seeing the lightning and hearing
the thunder.

e) If it takes 3.4 seconds to hear an echo,
how far away is the cliff?

*Remember your physics — the sound
has to go there and back again.*

Substitution

Q1 If $p = 2$, $q = 3$, $r = 5$ and $s = 6$, find the values of these expressions:

a) $3p + q$

b) $2r - s$

c) $r - (p + q)$

d) $r + q^2$

e) $rq - p$

f) $pr - q^2$

g) $r^2 - p^3$

h) $2p + 3q - 3s$

Q2 $k = \dfrac{x}{x - 2}$ Find the value of k when:

a) $x = 3$

b) $x = 1$

c) $x = 0$

d) $x = -2$

e) $x = -5$

f) $x = 0.5$

You could do this on a spreadsheet.

My best mate's a badger,
He wears a big moustache,
He spits real far
At the opera
And he belches with panache...

Q3 $k = \dfrac{3 - x}{x^2 - 5}$ Find the value of k when:

a) $x = 3$

b) $x = 1$

c) $x = 0$

d) $x = -2$

e) $x = -5$

f) $x = 0.5$

You could do this on a spreadsheet.

Q4 This formula finds the sum of all the numbers from 1 to n.

$$S_n = \frac{n(n + 1)}{2}$$

a) Calculate the sum of the first 15 numbers.

b) Calculate the sum of the first 25 numbers.

c) Use your answers to a) and b) to calculate the sum $16 + 17 + \ldots + 24 + 25$.

d) Calculate the sum of all the numbers from 3001 to 3405.

Deriving Formulas

Q1   Here are two triangular prisms.

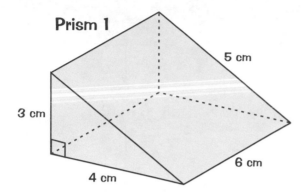

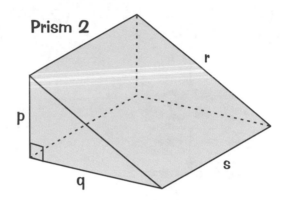

a) Calculate the area of the triangular cross-section of Prism 1.

b) Write an equation for the area A of the triangular cross-section of Prism 2.

c) Calculate the total surface area of Prism 1.

d) Write an equation for the total surface area S of Prism 2.

e) Calculate the volume of Prism 1.

f) Write an equation for the total volume V of Prism 2.

g) Use your formulas from d) and f) to calculate the surface area and volume
    of a prism with p = 2.5 cm, q = 6 cm, r = 6.5 cm, s = 53 cm.

Q2   Adam has a horses and Bruce has b horses. In each of the cases below, write an equation
relating a and b, and use it to work out how many horses Adam would have if Bruce had 100.

a) Adam has 3 times as many horses as Bruce.

b) Adam has 3 more than twice as many horses as Bruce.

c) Adam has 20 more than Bruce.

d) If Bruce gave 5 horses to Adam, then they would have equal numbers.

e) Half of Adam's horses plus twice Bruce's equals three times Adam's.

Practise this maths — don't prism you know it...

I once had a horse. No, actually, I didn't, I had fifty. Fifty-five horses. And they could speak and everything. They did all
my homework for me and they were cool and wore designer suits. I thought those horses were great. But they went away...

Generating Sequences

Q1   Here are three flow charts.

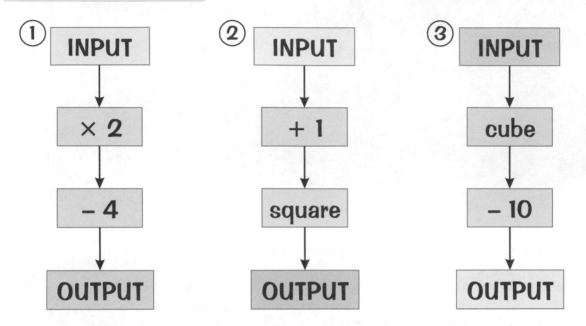

For each chart, work out the output when the input is:

a) 1   c) 3   e) -10

b) 2   d) 10

Q2   Use this flow chart, and a calculator or spreadsheet,
to find the output for inputs 1, 2, 3, 4 etc.

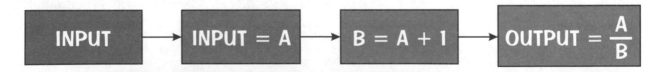

a) What sequence does this generate?

b) What happens to the output as the input increases?

c) Check your prediction for inputs 10 and 100.

d) What do you think will be the output for
really HUMUNGOUS numbers?

Generating Sequences II

Q1 Describe in words the rule for finding the next term of each sequence, and write the next 3 terms.

a) 12, 14, 16

b) 224, 112, 56

c) 3, 6, 9, 12

d) 3, 6, 12, 24

e) 8, 6, 4, 2

f) -13, -10, -7, -4

g) -5, -8, -11, -14

h) 1, 4, 9, 16

Come 'ere cheeky.

Q2 The rule for a sequence is "double the previous term and subtract 3". Use this rule to write the next four terms if the first term is:

a) 4

b) 3

c) 0

d) 100

e) -20

f) 0.5

g) 0.25

h) 3.1

Q3 Write the first 3 terms, plus the 10th term and the 25th term of each sequence.

a) nth term = $4n - 2$

b) nth term = $10 - n$

c) nth term = $7n - 2$

d) nth term = $100 - 2n$

e) nth term = $5n - 12$

f) nth term = n^2

g) nth term = $\dfrac{n}{2} + 3$

h) nth term = $n(n + 2)$

Q4 Sequence A has nth term $2n - 1$, and sequence B has nth term $2n + 1$.

a) Write down the first 4 terms of each sequence and comment on what you find.

b) How could you use this information to write alternate numbers starting at 23?

c) Write down an expression to generate all the even numbers starting at 42.

Sequences from Practical Contexts

Q1 Here is a pattern sequence:

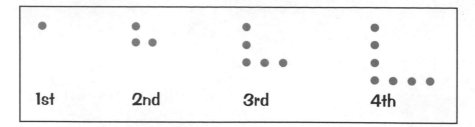

1st 2nd 3rd 4th

a) Copy and complete this sequence table:

pattern number	1	2	3	4	5	6	7	8
number of dots								

b) How many dots will there be in the 10th and 30th pattern?

c) How many dots will there be in the nth pattern?

Hint: Drawing the next couple of patterns might help.

Q2 Repeat question 1 for this pattern sequence.

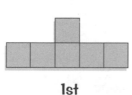
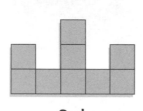
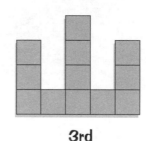

1st 2nd 3rd

Q3 This is a pattern made with different colour squares.

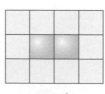
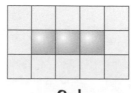

1st 2nd 3rd

I've been low-res since 1964.

a) Construct a sequence table for dark squares and light squares.

b) How many of each colour will be needed for the 50th pattern?

c) How many of each colour will be needed for the nth pattern?

d) How many tiles in total will be needed for the nth pattern? Comment on your answer.

Functions and Mapping Diagrams

Q1 Use a spreadsheet or calculator to complete these function tables.

a)

x→	3x + 2
0	
1	
2	
3	
4	
5	
6	

c)

x→	2x − 5
0	
1	
2	
3	
4	
5	
6	

e)

x→	4 − x
0	
1	
2	
3	
4	
5	
6	

b)

x→	x + 5
-3	
-2	
-1	
0	
1	
2	
3	

d)

x→	6 − ½x
0	
1	
2	
3	
4	
5	
6	

f)

x→	x/4 + 1
-3	
-2	
-1	
0	
1	
2	
3	

Show each function on a mapping line like this:

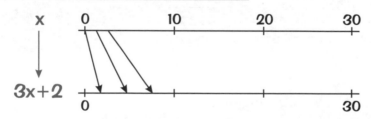

What do you notice that is different about the "shape" of functions d) and e)?

Q2 Draw mapping diagrams for these functions.

a) $x \rightarrow 2x$

b) $x \rightarrow 3x$

c) $x \rightarrow -2x$

d) $x \rightarrow \frac{1}{2}x$

Properties of Functions

Q1 Complete the operators for each box.

INPUT

2, 4, 6, 8 → [   ] → 4, 8, 12, 16 → [   ] → 8, 12, 16, 20

2, 4, 6, 8 → [   ] → 4, 6, 8, 10 → [   ] → 8, 12, 16, 20

Q2 Give one possible operator for each function. Write the function as "x →"

a) input 1, 3, 5, 7 → [   ] → output 6, 10, 14, 18

Example: x → 2x + 4

b) input 3, 6, 9, 12 → [   ] → output -1, 0, 1, 2

c) input 26, 24, 30, 20 → [   ] → output 17, 16, 19, 14

d) input 35, 55, 65, 45 → [   ] → output 3, 7, 9, 5

Q3 Simplify these function machines and give your answer as "x →"

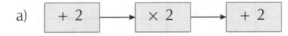

a)   [+ 2] → [× 2] → [+ 2]

Example: x → 2(x + 2) + 2
i.e. x → 2x + 6

b)   [− 1] → [× 3] → [+ 6]

c)   [+ 6] → [× 2] → [+ 4]

d)   [+ 2] → [× 6] → [+ 4] → [÷ 2]

Q4 Write the inverse for each of the following functions.

Check your answers by putting some numbers in.

a) $x \rightarrow 2x$

e) $x \rightarrow x - 107$

b) $x \rightarrow 4x$

f) $x \rightarrow 2x + 3$

c) $x \rightarrow \frac{1}{2}x$

g) $x \rightarrow 3(x + 3)$

d) $x \rightarrow x + 34$

h) $x \rightarrow \frac{x}{3} + 4$

Input "my dog's got no nose" → add "how does it smell"...

That hint "check your answers by putting some numbers in" is a good 'un. Pick an easy number to be *x* (like 2 or 3), and stick it into the original question, *and then put the result into your inverse to see if you get back to the number you started with.* Now what could be simpler than that...

Plotting Graphs

Q1   Complete this table of values for the function $y = 2x - 4$.

x	-3	-2	-1	0	1	2	3
y = 2x − 4							

a) Draw axes with $-10 \leq x \leq 10$ and $-10 \leq y \leq 10$.

Translation: this means with x and y having values from -10 to +10

b) Plot your values from the table to draw the line $y = 2x - 4$.

c) Use your graph to find the value of y when $x = 1.5$.

d) Use your graph to find the value of x when $y = -3$.

e) On the same axes draw the line $y = 2x + 3$.

f) Where does each line cross the y-axis?

g) What is the gradient of each line?

Gradient: How far up you go for every one you go from left to right

Q2   Draw one set of axes with $-10 \leq x \leq 10$ and $-10 \leq y \leq 10$.

a) Make a table of values for each of these functions, and plot each line on the same graph.

$$y = x + 4, \qquad y = 3x, \qquad y = x - 1, \qquad y = \frac{1}{2}x + 2, \qquad y = 4$$

b) Write down the equations of two lines that are parallel.

c) Write down the equations of two lines that pass through (-4, 0).

d) Write the coordinates of another point that is on two lines.

e) Could you have answered b) without bothering to draw the lines?

Q3   Write the equation of the line that passes through each of these sets of points.

a) (2, 1) (2, 2) (2, 3) (2, 7)

b) (5, 5) (7, 7) (9, 9) (11, 11)

c) (2, 0) (3, 0) (6, 0) (11, 0)

d) (1, 2) (2, 4) (3, 6) (4, 8)

y = mx + c

Q1   Match each line to its correct equation.

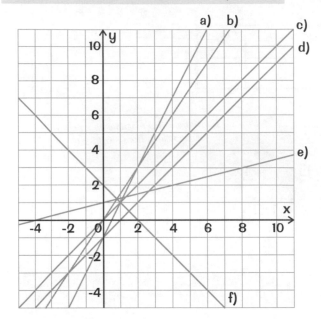

a)   b)   c)
d)
e)
f)

$y = x$

$y = 2x - 1$

$y = \dfrac{3}{2}x$

$y = 2 - x$

$y = \dfrac{1}{4}x + 1$

$y = x - 1$

Hint: Fit the x and y coordinates of a point on the line into the equation to check if it is true.

If you've got time, you could bung these into a spreadsheet or a graphical calculator to get a better idea of it.

Q2   Draw one set of axes with x and y from -10 to 10.
Then draw the "family" of lines:

$y = 2x$ $y = 2x + 1$ $y = 2x + 2$ $y = 2x - 3$

a) What do you notice about
   the gradient of these lines?

b) What about the intercept?

Intercept means where the line crosses the y-axis.

c) Use this information to add the lines $y = 2x + 5$ and $y = 2x - \dfrac{1}{2}$ to your "family".

Q3   Draw this "family" of lines:

$y = x$ $y = 2x$ $y = 3x$ $y = 0.5x$

a) What do you notice about the gradient of these lines?

b) What about the intercept?

c) Use this information to add the lines $y = 4x$ and $y = \dfrac{1}{4}x$ to your "family".

"Family of Lions"
...It was funny in my head.

Q4   Without using a table of values SKETCH these lines.

a) $y = x + 3$ c) $y = \dfrac{1}{2}x + 3$

b) $y = 2x - 4$ d) $y = 6x + 1$

y = mx + c — almost a song by the Village People...

"m is the gradient, c is the intercept"   Remember that.
(*Gradient* is the slope of the line, and *intercept* is where the line crosses the y-axis.)

Graphs of Real-Life Problems

Q1 a) Copy these axes and use them to show the following
    information about Cleopatra's chariot ride to the forum.

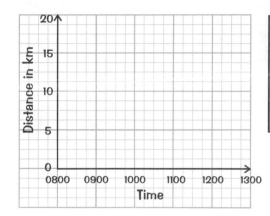

She leaves home at 0900.

The forum is 15 km away and she arrives at 0945.

She spends 1 hour shopping and drinking Asses' milk.

She then sets off for home, arriving at 1200.

Note: She travels at a constant speed while going to and from the forum.

b) How fast does she travel on her way to the shops?

c) How fast does she travel on her way home?

Q2 These graphs shows the depth of water (*d*) against time (*t*) after the
    taps have been opened. Match each tank to its correct graph.

Hint: The water flows out of each tap at the same constant rate.

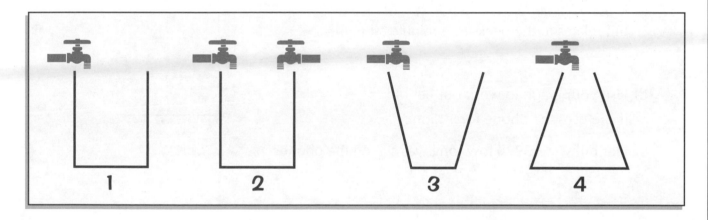

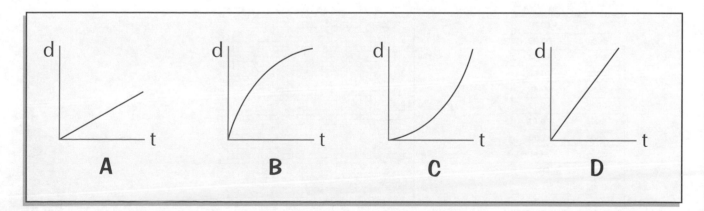

Interpreting Graphs

Q1   Each graph shows the motion of an object.
Explain in words what is shown in the following graphs.

a)
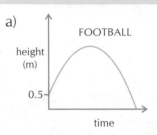
FOOTBALL
height (m)
0.5
time

c)
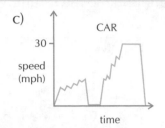
CAR
30
speed (mph)
time

e)
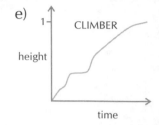
CLIMBER
1
height
time

b)
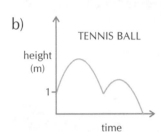
TENNIS BALL
height (m)
1
time

d)
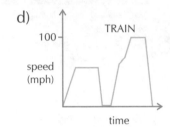
TRAIN
100
speed (mph)
time

Q2   Portia's mobile phone bill is calculated as follows:
£17 per month plus 5p per minute for all peak-time calls.

a) Calculate her bill if she makes 60 mins of peak-time calls.

b) Calculate her bill if she makes 200 mins of peak-time calls.

c) Copy these axes, and then plot a line to show how her bill relates to the peak-time minutes she uses.

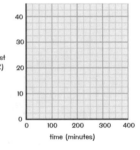

cost (£)
40
30
20
10
0
0   100   200   300   400
time (minutes)

d) Use your graph to work out her bill if she uses the phone for 145 mins.

e) Her bill was £32. How long was she on the phone?

Q3   Copy these axes, and plot the postage price information for second-class post.

Weight up to	2nd Class Cost
60g	£0.19
100g	£0.33
150g	£0.44
200g	£0.54
250g	£0.66
300g	£0.76
350g	£0.87
400g	£1.00
450g	£1.14
500g	£1.30
600g	£1.52
700g	£1.74
750g	£1.85

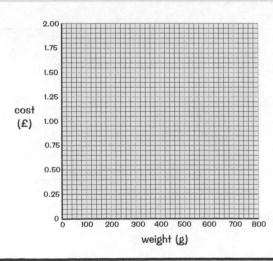

cost (£)
2.00
1.75
1.50
1.25
1.00
0.75
0.50
0.25
0
0   100   200   300   400   500   600   700   800
weight (g)

Want some post eh sonny, eh, eh?

Angles

Q1   Find all the missing angles in these triangles.

Make sure that you describe each angle correctly e.g. ABC = 80°.

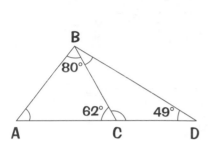

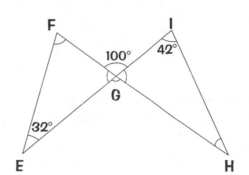

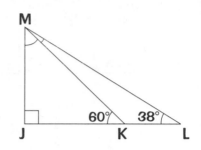

Q2   In each diagram find all the angles labelled. In each case write down your reasoning.

e.g. the angle is opposite to.........
the angle is corresponding to.........
the angle is alternate to.........

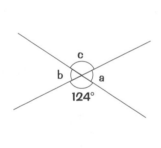

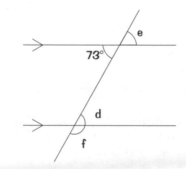

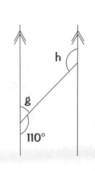

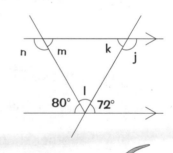

Q3   Find the angles marked, explaining how you know in every case.

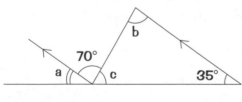

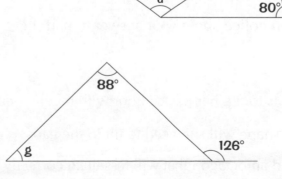

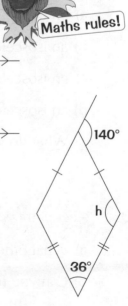

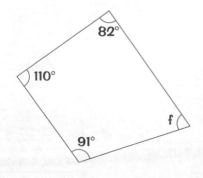

Sketching 2D Shapes

Q1   Tessellate these shapes. You should draw at least 6 more shapes for each.

 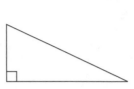 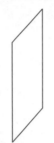 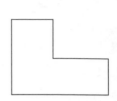

Q2   Which of the following shapes will tessellate?

       A: equilateral triangle   E: regular hexagon

       B: scalene triangle   F: regular octagon

       C: kite   G: regular pentagon

       D: trapezium   H: rhombus

Q3   Draw any two identical right-angled triangles and cut them out.

     a) Put them together to form two different triangles. What sort of triangles are they?

     b) What other shape can you make from these two triangles?

Q4   What angles do you get in triangles made by folding:

     a) an equilateral triangle in half along a line of symmetry?

     b) an isosceles triangle with angles 70°, 70°, 40° along its line of symmetry?

     c) an isosceles triangle with angles 10°, 160°, 10° along its line of symmetry?

     d) an isosceles triangle with angles 90°, 45°, 45° along its line of symmetry?

        What do you notice about your answer to part d)?

Q5   Cleopatra wants to tile her palace floor with regular octagonal tiles.

     a) What other shape will she need to fill in the gaps?

     b) Can you find an octagon that will tessellate correctly without gaps?

L'eau de Bog
For silky soft skin

Triangles and Quadrilaterals

Q1 Match these quadrilaterals to their correct properties.
(There may be more than one property for each.)

square

rectangle

parallelogram

rhombus

kite

trapezium

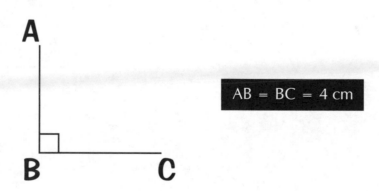

4 equal sides

4 right angles

just 1 pair of equal angles

2 opposite pairs of equal sides

2 pairs of equal angles

diagonals equal in length

2 adjacent pairs of equal sides

diagonals intersect at 90°

only 1 pair of parallel sides

2 pairs of parallel sides

Q2 Sketch 2 different isosceles triangles with at least one angle of 40°.

Q3 Draw this shape accurately.

A

B **C**

AB = BC = 4 cm

a) Use compasses to construct the point D, where AD = CD = 8 cm and ABCD is a kite.

b) Use compasses to construct the point E, where AE = CE = 8 cm and ABCD is an arrowhead.

c) Measure the angle ADC and AEC. What do you notice?

d) What shape is ADCE?

e) Measure the angles BAD and BAE.

Before   ...after

Crusty isosceles — loave triangle...

Look what that fat ugly bloodsucker did to my prize cow.

Congruence

Q1 Match these shapes into congruent pairs.

Hint: Tracing paper may help!

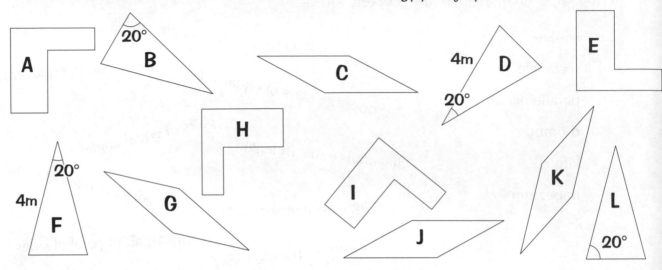

Q2 Mark these pairs **congruent**, **not congruent** or **don't know**.

a)

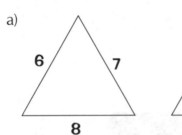

b)

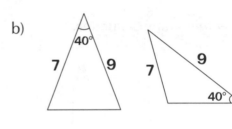

c)

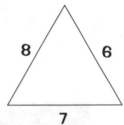

d)

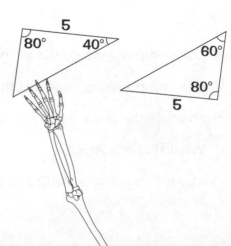

e)

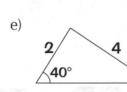   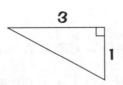   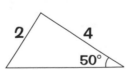

Almost congruent...   *Almost congruent...*

Congruence is a stupid maths name that just means "the same size and shape". They look easy, but you can muck them up if you rush 'em. Check each one even if you think you don't need to.

Plans and Elevations

Q1   Complete this table. The first column has been done for you.

3D					
name	cube				
net					
faces	6				
edges	12				
vertices	8				

Q2   Draw nets for the following shapes.

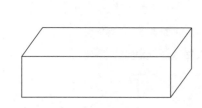
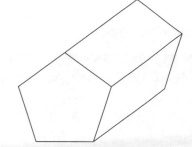
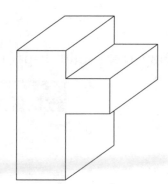

Q3   Here are the nets of four cubes.

```
    1  2  3                5  3            3  5                    6  4
A      4           B    1  2          C    1              D       1
       5                   4               2                   2  5
       6                   6               6  4                   3
```

a) For each cube decide which number is on the face opposite:

    i) the 1   ii) the 2

b) Which of the four is a "proper" dice?

The evil dice hoards will
never take CleaverGirl alive.

Isometric Drawings

Q1 Use isometric paper to draw:

a) a cube with sides 3 units,

b) a cuboid with sides 2 units, 3 units and 4 units,

c) two different shapes each made with 6 cubic bricks.

Q2 Draw the plan, front view (elevation) and side elevation for each of these shapes.

a) 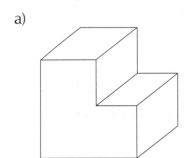 b) 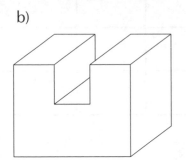 c)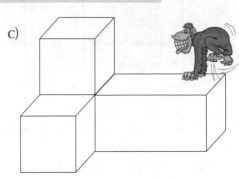

Q3 Draw these solid shapes on isometric paper.

	PLAN	FRONT ELEVATION	SIDE ELEVATION
a)			
b)			
c)			
d)			

Transformations

Q1 Here are some patterns. Copy each pattern and continue it for 3 more units.
Describe how each pattern is made from the first shape.
Then design two more patterns using the same base unit.

a)

b)

c)

d)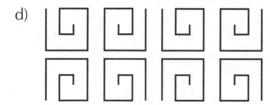

Q2 Trace this diagram and reflect the shape in
the mirror lines to form three new images.

[There's more than one possible answer.]

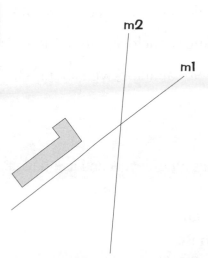

Q3 Write down all the capital letters in the alphabet that have:

It can depend on how you write your letters, so assume each one is as symmetrical as possible.

a) 1 line of symmetry

b) More than 1 line of symmetry

c) Rotational symmetry

d) Both rotational and line symmetry

e) No symmetry at all

WHERE'S ALL
MY MONKEYS????

Section Five — Shape, Space and Measures

Transformations - II

Q1   Draw a set of axes with x and y values from -6 to 6.

a) Plot the triangle with vertices A (1, 1) B (1, 4) and C (3, 4).

b) Reflect ABC in the y-axis and label it $A_1B_1C_1$.

c) Rotate ABC 180° about (0, 0) and label it $A_2B_2C_2$.

d) Rotate ABC 90° clockwise about (0, 0) and label it $A_3B_3C_3$.

e) Reflect ABC in the x-axis and label it $A_4B_4C_4$.

Q2   Draw a set of axes with x from -9 and 9, and y from -6 to 6.

a) Plot the figure DEFG where D is (-2, 1), E is (-2, 3), F is (-4, 3), G is (-5, 1).

b) Rotate DEFG 90° clockwise about (0, 0) — label it $D_1E_1F_1G_1$.

c) Rotate DEFG 90° anticlockwise about (0, 0) — label it $D_2E_2F_2G_2$.

d) Rotate DEFG 90° clockwise about (-2, 1) — label it $D_3E_3F_3G_3$.

e) Rotate DEFG 90° clockwise about (2, -3) — label it $D_4E_4F_4G_4$.

f) Rotate DEFG 90° anticlockwise about (4, 5) — label it $D_5E_5F_5G_5$.

g) Rotate DEFG 90° anticlockwise about (-3, 2) — label it $D_6E_6F_6G_6$.

Q3   This graph shows an object A and its image B.

a) What single transformation moves A onto B?

b) Find one combination of transformations that will also move A onto B.

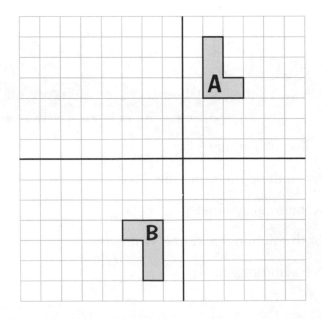

Transformations — Enlargement

Q1   Here is an object and its images K and L.

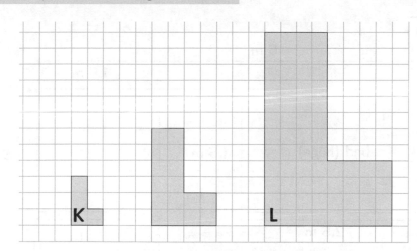 

a) What scale factor enlarges the object onto image L?

b) What scale factor enlarges the object onto image K?

c) What scale factor enlarges K onto L?

Q2   Copy this shape.

 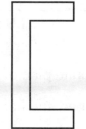

a) Enlarge it scale factor 2, centre X, to make image A.

b) Enlarge it scale factor 3, centre X, to make image B.

c) Enlarge it scale factor 4, centre X, to make image C.

Q3   On a graph with both axes from -6 to 6, draw triangle
ABC where A = (1, 1), B = (2, 1) and C = (1, 3).

a) Enlarge ABC by scale factor 2, centre (0, 0) and write down its new coordinates.

b) Enlarge ABC by scale factor 2, centre (3, 3) and write down its new coordinates.

c) Enlarge ABC by scale factor 2, centre (1, 1) and write down its new coordinates.

d) Find an enlargement of scale factor 4, that will make an image in the fourth quadrant.

Remember: the fourth quadrant is the bottom right hand quarter of the graph.

A great page for L spotters...

You need to get 2 things right to do an enlargement transformation — the "scale factor" and the "centre of enlargement". If you don't know how, get back to that revision guide sharpish.

Scales and Scale Drawings

Q1   Here is Ophelia's bedroom.

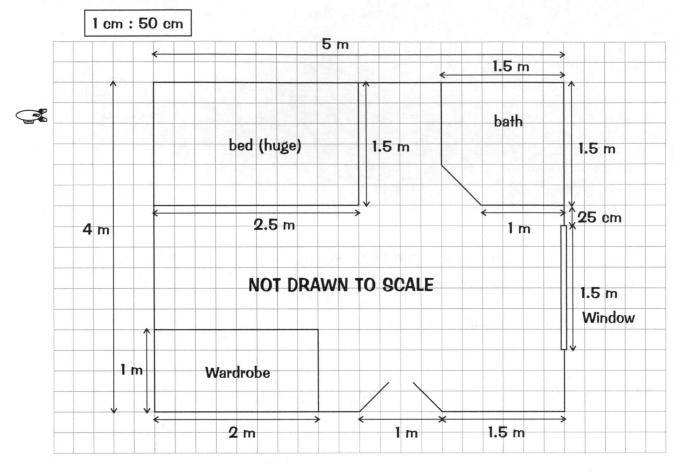

1 cm : 50 cm

5 m

1.5 m

bed (huge)

1.5 m

bath

1.5 m

4 m

2.5 m

1 m

25 cm

NOT DRAWN TO SCALE

1.5 m

Window

1 m

Wardrobe

2 m

1 m

1.5 m

a) Using a scale of 1 cm to represent 50 cm, draw an accurate plan of her bedroom.

b) Can she fit a mirror 1 m wide on the wall between her bed and her wardrobe?

c) What are the dimensions of the biggest sofa that will fit to the right of the door without obscuring the window?

Q2   On a plan of the city, Portia measures the distance from the hairdressers to the market as 9 cm. If the scale of the plan is given as 1 : 5000, how far will she have to walk?

Q3   Macbeth measures the distance from Birnam Wood to Dunsinane as 9.5 cm on his map. The actual distance is 19 km.

a) Write the actual distance from Birnam Wood to Dunsinane in cm.

b) Write the ratio distance on map : actual distance.

c) What is the scale of his map? Write your answer as "1 cm represents ? km" and as a ratio 1 : ?.

d) Using the same map he measures the distance to Perth as 8 cm. How far must he march?

Coordinates

Q1   Draw a set of axes -10 ≤ x ≤ 10 and -10 ≤ y ≤ 10.
Plot each set of coordinates and join them to form a letter.

a) (-9,6)   (-9,9)   (-7,8)   (-5,9)   (-5,6)

b) (-4,5)   (-2,8)   (0,5)   (-1,6.5)   (-3,6.5)

c) (0,7)   (3,7)   (1.5,7)   (1.5,3)

d) (4,2)   (4,6)   (4,4)   (6,4)   (6,6)   (6,2)

e) (9,5)   (7,5)   (7,3)   (9,3)   (9,1)   (7,1)

f) (-9,-4)   (-9,-6)

g) (-8,-4)   (-9,-4)   (-9,-5)   (-8,-5)   (-8,-6)   (-9,-6)

h) (-1,-4)   (-4,-4)   (-4,-9)   (-1,-9)

i) (1,-3)   (4,-3)   (4,-8)   (1,-8)

j) (5,-2)   (5,-7)   (8,-7)   (8,-2)

k) (9,-1)   (9,-6)   (10,-6)

DANGER!
If the fall doesn't get you the
marketingexec-headed
anaconda will.

Q2   Plot each pair of points, join with a line and write
down the coordinates of the midpoint of the line.

a)   (3,3)   (7,3)   e)   (5,2)   (7,3)

b)   (-1,4)   (-1,-4)   f)   (-3,-4)   (3,4)

c)   (2,2)   (4,4)   g)   (1,-6)   (3,7)

d)   (-2,0)   (0,-2)   h)   (-4,3)   (-1,0)

Q3   Plot any rectangle and write down its coordinates.

a) Draw the two diagonals.

b) Write down the coordinates of the point where they intersect.

c) How could you have predicted the coordinates from the coordinates of the rectangle?

d) Draw a different rectangle and check your findings.

(over, there) (by the pigeon, under the dog)...

x is across (a... cross) and y is up and down. x coordinate is always first, followed by y. It's not
hard — x before y, x before y, x before y, x before y, x before y, x before y, x before y, x before y, x before y...

<u>Constructing Triangles</u>

Q1 Using compasses and a ruler construct these triangles.

    a) triangle ABC with AB = 7 cm, BC = 5 cm, CA = 3 cm.

    b) triangle DEF with DE = 8 cm, EF = 5.5 cm, FD = 6 cm.

    c) triangle GHI with GH = HI = IG = 6.5 cm.

    d) triangle JKL with JK = 9.3 cm, KL = 4.5 cm, LJ = 7.5 cm.

Q2 Draw accurately each of these triangles.

    a) triangle MNP with angle M = 30 °, MN = 6 cm, MP = 5 cm.

    b) triangle QRS with angle R = 70°, QR = 9.3 cm, SR = 5.5 cm.

    c) triangle TUV with angle V = 50°, VT = 7 cm, UV = 9 cm.

    d) triangle WXY with angle X = 80°, XW = XY, = 7 cm.

    What do you notice about triangles TUV and WXY?

Q3 Draw accurately each of these triangles.

    a) triangle PTO with angle P = 30°, angle T = 60°, PT = 7 cm.

    b) triangle TLC with angle T = 40°, angle C = 35°, TC = 6.6 cm.

    c) triangle GSH with angle S = 112°, angle H = 35°, SH = 8.3 cm.

    d) triangle PDQ with angle P = 28°, angle D = 39°, PD = 5.8 cm.

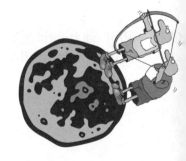

Q4 Using compasses (and no protractor) construct an angle of 60°.

    Bisect your angle to make an angle of 30°.

Q5 Draw two points 8 cm apart.   Label them A and B.
Draw the locus of all the points which are equidistant from A and B.

Q6 Draw 3 points and label them D, E and F.
By constructing perpendicular bisectors find the point which is equidistant from all three points.

 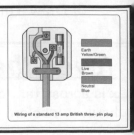

Simple Loci

Q1 A knight on a chessboard can move in any direction by going EITHER 2 squares forward then 1 sideways OR 1 square forward and 2 sideways. Use squared paper to draw the locus of all its possible positions after 1 move. Repeat this for the King who can move 1 square in any direction.

Q2 SKETCH a possible locus of each of the following.

a) A goat grazing tethered on a rope 10 m long.

b) A conker swinging on a 40 cm string.

c) A rugby ball after it has been kicked for goal.

d) A tennis ball in play.

e) A plane taking off from a runway.

f) A dog tied to the corner of a house.

There are many possible answers — compare yours with your friends.

Q3 Superman must pass between a spider and a snake which are 5 m apart. He is equally terrified of both.

a) Sketch the path he must take to keep as safe as possible.

b) Describe his route and construct an accurate scale drawing.

That means use complicated maths-speak words. Don't forget to write down your scale on the diagram!

Q4 A light aircraft is flying from A to B. Draw the diagram using a scale of 1 cm to 1 km.

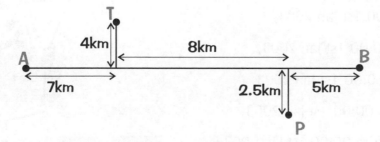

a) There is a thunderstorm over T with a radius of 5 km which must be avoided. Draw the storm-affected area on your diagram.

b) Planes cannot fly within a 3 km "no-fly" zone over a royal palace at P. Add this to your diagram.

c) The pilot can only fly in straight lines. Draw a possible route he can take from A to B.

Measurements — Units

Q1   Choose an appropriate unit from each list to measure the following.

a) The weight of a mouse.

b) The height of a camel.

c) The length of a garden.

d) The area of a field.

e) The distance to the seaside.

f) The dimensions of a book.

g) The weight of a dog.

h) The capacity of a car petrol tank.

i) The capacity of a bottle of wine.

metric	imperial
gram	inch
metre	yard
centimetre	pound
litre	mile
kilogram	gallon
hectare	acre
kilometre	ounce
centilitre	pint
	ton
	foot

Q2   Write the following.

a) 4500 g in kg

b) 7.75 m in cm

c) 7.75 m in mm

d) 8435 m in km

e) 7 tonnes in kg

f) 7 tonnes in g

g) 6.3 litres in ml

h) 800 ml in litres

i) 6 cm in mm

j) 4.2 ha in m^2

Q3   Work out the date and time:

a) 35 days after 00:00 1st Jan 2003,

b) 135 hours after 00:00 1st Jan 2003,

c) 363.5 days after 00:00 1st Jan 2003,

d) 10 000 mins after 00:00 1st Jan 2003,

e) 1000 seconds before 00:00 1st Jan 2003,

f) 1 century, 3 decades, 2 years and 4 days after 12:30 Jan 30th 2003.

Uniting units — centikilometregramton...

Learn what the basic units are — you can probably guess how big a metre is, but can you guess
how heavy a gram is or how much is in a gallon? If not get a gram and a gallon and find out.

Bearings

Q1 Write each of these directions as a three-figure bearing.

"Just say what you see."

Hint: South South West is half-way between South and South West

a) East

b) South

c) North

d) West

e) South-east

f) North-east

g) South-south-west

h) South-west

i) North-north-east

j) North-west

Q2 Mark a town L in the centre of a page. Using a scale of 1 cm : 5 km, mark the position of each place using its bearing from L.

a) Sumburgh 193° 33 km

b) Papa Stour 300° 35 km

c) Ulsta 000° 38 km

d) Fetlar 017° 52 km

e) Noss 105° 8 km

f) Foula 265° 49 km

g) Where are these places?

h) What is the name of L?

Q3 Use this map to measure and write down the bearing and distance of:

p.s. this spotty giant's face is absolutely flat and horizontal.

a) The mole from zit 3.

b) The bogey from zit 3.

c) Zit 1 from zit 3.

d) Zit 1 from zit 2.

e) The bogey from zit 1.

f) Zit 4 from the bogey.

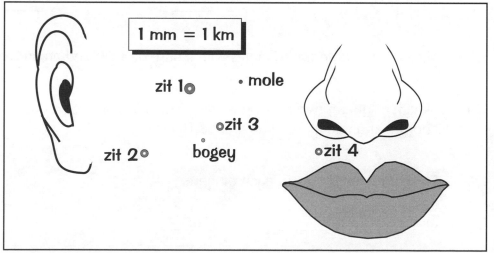

Q4 If St Ives is on a bearing of 035° from Penzance, what is the bearing of Penzance from St Ives?

Q5 If Thurso is on a bearing of 220° from Kirkwall, what is the bearing of Kirkwall from Thurso?

Areas

Q1 Calculate the areas of the following shapes.

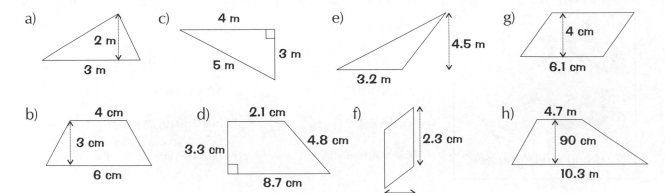

a) 2 m 3 m

c) 4 m 3 m 5 m

e) 4.5 m 3.2 m

g) 4 cm 6.1 cm

b) 4 cm 3 cm 6 cm

d) 2.1 cm 3.3 cm 4.8 cm 8.7 cm

f) 2.3 cm 1.8 cm

h) 4.7 m 90 cm 10.3 m

Q2 Calculate the areas of the following shapes.

Hint: sometimes it's easiesr to draw a rectangle around the shape and then subtract the areas that you DON'T need.

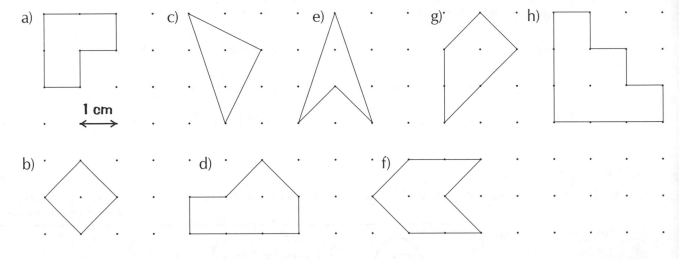

a)   1 cm

c)

e)

g)

h)

b)

d)

f)

Q3 Sketch three different triangles with a base of 4 cm and an area of 12 cm^2.

Q4 Sketch a square, two rectangles, two parallelograms, two trapeziums and one triangle all with an area of 16 cm^2.

Q5 Find the shaded area in each of these.

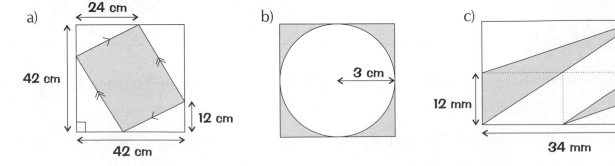

a) 24 cm 42 cm 42 cm 12 cm

b) 3 cm

c) 12 mm 34 mm 6 mm

Volume and Displacement

Q1   Find the volumes of these shapes.

a)
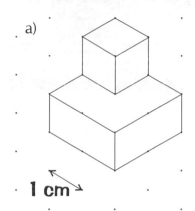

1 cm

b)
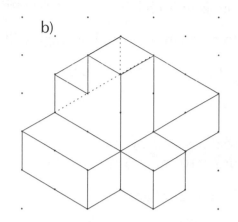

c)
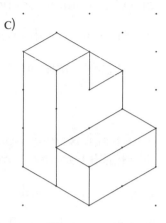

Q2   Find the volumes of the following cuboids.

a) 3 cm × 4 cm × 5 cm

b) 10 cm × 5 cm × 2.5 cm

c) 6 ft × 2 ft × 3 ft

Don't forget to give your units each time.

d) 7.1 m × 4.2 m × 0.2 m

e) 56 cm × 23 cm × 50 mm

f) 0.25 m × 1.2 m × 0.8 m

g) Give your answers to d) and f) in cm³.

Q3   Portia is calculating the volumes of things in her kitchen.
Use estimation to check her calculations, then correct those she has wrong.

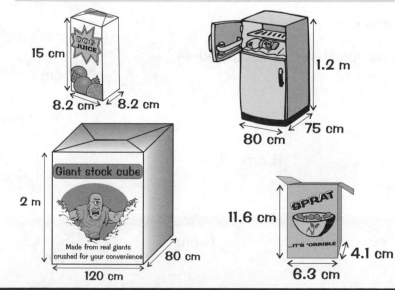

15 cm

8.2 cm   8.2 cm

1.2 m

80 cm   75 cm

2 m

Giant stock cube

Made from real giants
crushed for your convenience

120 cm   80 cm

11.6 cm

6.3 cm   4.1 cm

Volumes:
Fridge = under 7200 cm³
Cereal box = 299.628 cm³
Juice carton = 131.2 cm³
Giant stock cube = 19200 cm³

Section Five — Shape, Space and Measures

Solving Problems

Q1 Shylock is making chocolate bars. He has 4.8 litres of melted chocolate to make 100 identical bars.

    a) What volume of chocolate is in each bar?   *Hint: convert to cm³ first*

    b) If the base of the bar is to be 4 cm × 6 cm, how high will it be?

    c) Suggest three other sets of dimensions that the bar could have.

Q2 Oberon has stolen some gold from the pixies. He has 8 bars, each measuring 10 cm × 6 cm × 2 cm.

    a) Calculate the volume of each bar of gold.

    b) He melts down all the bars. What is the total volume of gold?

    c) He recasts them as cubes with side 3 cm. How many complete cubes can he make?

Q3 Titania has made some turkish delight. Each piece is 1.5 cm × 2.5 cm × 3 cm, and she wants to store it in boxes that measure 10 cm × 9 cm × 8 cm.

    a) Calculate the volume of each sweet.   *Hint: draw a sketch*

    b) Work out the maximum number of sweets that she can fit in each box.

    c) Calculate the volume of the box.

    d) Calculate the volume of air in each box when it is filled with sweets.

Q4 For each shape work out: a) the volume,

                            b) the surface area,

                            c) the total length of all the edges.

Shape 1: 5 cm, 3 cm, 2 cm

Shape 2: 1 cm, 3 cm, 1 cm, 2 cm, 4 cm

Shape 3: 2 cm, 2 cm, 2 cm, 4 cm, 6 cm, 10 cm

Data Collection Methods

Q1 The box below contains three different methods for collecting data.
Choose the most suitable method for collecting data in the situations listed.

> **1** survey / observation   **2** experiment   **3** secondary data

a) Methods of travel to school.

b) How long Year 8 pupils can hold their breath.

c) Traffic flows on the local bypass.

d) Life expectancy of women.

e) Weight of pupils in Class 6B.

f) Number of cars per family in the UK.

g) Crime figures in your area.

h) Favourite television programmes of teachers in your school.

Q2 Plan an experiment to measure the reaction time of pupils in your school.

Consider the following:

(i)   What will you use to test reaction time?

(ii) Who will you test?

(iii) How many people will you test?

(iv) How will you try to ensure your results represent the reaction times of pupils in the whole school?

Class 6B looking ready for action.

I like the sci-fi channel.

Q3 Design a questionnaire to investigate favourite TV programmes.

Consider the following:

(i)   What questions will you ask?

(ii) Who will you ask?

(iii) How many people will you ask?

Q4 How would you choose a random sample of people in your area from the phone book?
What are the advantages and disadvantages of this method of sampling?

What a wonderful data collect some data...

There are different ways to collect data, and the best one to use will depend on the situation.
But if you're doing a survey, you have to make sure you ask lots of different people.

Collecting Data — Frequency Tables

Q1 Copy and complete this data collection sheet for house prices in your area.
Use a local paper to decide on suitable price bands, and how many bands you will need.

Price band	Tally	Frequency
£?000 - £?000		
£?000 - £?000		
£?000 - £?000		
£?000 - £?000		
£?000 - £?000		

Q2 Construct a frequency table to record the number of goals scored per match.

France 0 - 1 Senegal	Japan 2 - 2 Belgium	England 1 - 0 Argentina	Costa Rica 1 - 1 Turkey
Germany 8 - 0 Saudi Arabia	South Korea 2 - 0 Poland	Sweden 2 - 1 Nigeria	USA 1 - 1 South Korea
Cameroon 1 - 1 Ireland	Argentina 1 - 1 Nigeria	Brazil 4 - 0 China	Japan 1 - 0 Russia
England 1 - 1 Sweden	Turkey 0 - 2 Brazil	Italy 1 - 2 Croatia	France 0 - 0 Uruguay

Q3 Design a frequency table to record the heights of pupils in Year 8 and Year 11.
Choose suitable group sizes and allow for both extremes.

Q4 Design a tally chart which could be used to collect data about the
traffic flow outside Mange Hill school. The data is being collected
to help decide whether a 'lollipop person' should be employed.

a) What days would you collect the data? And at what times?

b) What would you expect from data collected
Sunday lunchtime?

c) Sid the caretaker collected data from
8.30 - 9.30 every weekday morning
from June until September.
What would you expect his results to show?

Practise frequently — Dand you'll be table to do this easily...

They don't make the most interesting topic in the world, but frequency tables are easy and need to
be practised until you can make one with your eyes closed and your hands tied behind your back.

Two-Way Tables

Q1 Copy and complete this two-way table about the members of a sports club. Then use your table to answer the questions.

	Male	Female	Total
Junior	87	92	
Senior	245	351	
Total			

a) How many members are junior girls?

b) How many female members are there?

c) How many male members are there?

d) How many senior members are there?

e) How many members are there altogether?

f) Twins Jane and Susan, who are 9, and their father join the club.
Amend your table to include them, assuming that anyone under the age of 16 is a junior.

Q2 Copy and complete this two-way table to show how these people and animals are travelling. (I drew all the pictures myself, by the way.)

Bonzer (the dog) Claudia Dave

	Girl	Boy	Animal	Total
Walk				
Bike / trike				
Car				
Bus / coach				
Train				
Total				

Sharon Kevin

Rob Tracy Bob

Kylie Arthur (the dog)

Keith Rambo (the hedgehog)

Jason

Widget (the bird) Roger (the rabbit) Daphne Brad

Kelly Trevor (the pig)

Mean, Median, Mode and Range

Q1   Calculate the **mode** and **mean** of these sets of data.

a) 3 kg   4 kg   5 kg   5.5 kg   5.5 kg   6.6 kg   8.2 kg

b) 221   229   234   222   229   226   231   232   222   229

c) 5.2 m   4.7 m   8.1 m   4.3 m   7.9 m   8.1 m   6.7 m   7.6 m

d) 0.2   0.37   0.6   0.55   0.6   0.42   0.2

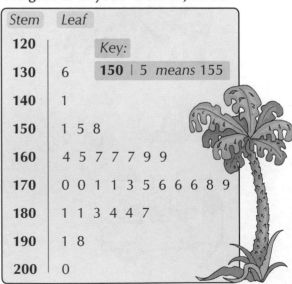

Q2   Calculate the **median** and **range** of these sets of data.

a) 33   35   38   41   49   50   50   51   52

b) 56 g   67 g   43 g   92 g   77 g   59 g   61 g

c) 56 cm   73 cm   67 cm   55 cm   46 cm   49 cm   57 cm   54 cm

d) 1004   1006   1007   1001   1003   1005

Q3   Copy this stem and leaf diagram and find:

a) The median height.

b) The range of heights.

c) The modal height.

d) Add these three new data points
   to your diagram.

   159 cm   135 cm   177 cm

   How do these extra points affect
   your answers to a), b) and c)?

Heights of boys in Class 6F, in cm

Stem	Leaf
120	
130	6
140	1
150	1 5 8
160	4 5 7 7 7 9 9
170	0 0 1 1 3 5 6 6 6 8 9
180	1 1 3 4 4 7
190	1 8
200	0

Key:
150 | 5 *means* 155

This page is mean and mode-y...

It's easy to get confused between the mean, the median and the mode. Just remember, the
<u>mode</u> is the one with <u>most</u>, the <u>median</u> is the <u>middle</u> one, and the mean is just mean to work out.

Calculating Statistics

Q1 Martin plays cricket, and in his last four innings he has made the following scores.

| 35 | 32 | 7 | 50 |

a) Calculate his **mean** score.

b) Calculate his **median** score.

c) Martin's batting average (mean) must be **at least 40** to get in the county side, and he has one more innings left. Calculate how many runs he needs to score if he is to get selected.

d) Do you think he will play for the county?

e) Do you care?

Q2 Calculate the **median** and **range** of this data.

Size of spider:

1.2 cm	1.6 cm	0.5 cm
0.7 cm	4.2 cm	0.2 cm
0.3 cm	3.8 cm	2.7 cm

Q3 Copy and complete the following sets of data so that the statistics shown are correct. (Each question mark represents one missing number.)

a) 3, 4, 5, 6, ?   with   *Range = 7, Median = 5*

b) 3, 5, 2, 8, 1, 2, ?   with   *Mean = 4*

c) 30, 28, 32, 29, ?, ?   with   *Mode = 28, Mean = 30*

d) 87, 87, 88, 88, 89, ?   with   *Range = 2, Mode = 88*

e) 4, 5, 6, 7, ?, ?   with   *Mean = 4.5, Mode = 4*

Q4 Write down 3 **different** sets of numbers, all with **mode = median = mean = 5**.

Q5 Write down 2 different sets of 8 numbers with the **same mean**, but where the **range of one set = twice the range of the other**.

Graphs and Diagrams

Q1 This chart shows **road deaths per 100,000 of population** for various countries in 1999.

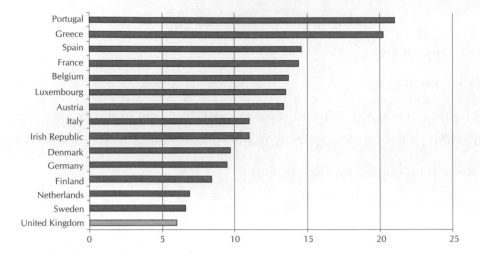

a) Which country has the worst fatality record for 1999?

b) Which country has the best record?

The populations of Sweden, Spain and the UK are approximately 9 million, 39 million and 59 million respectively.

c) Work out the approximate number of people who died on the roads in each of these three countries.

Q2 This table shows the holiday destinations of families in one street.
Copy the table and fill in the angle that each destination would take up in a pie chart.

	Frequency	Angle
None	21	
UK	48	
Europe	29	
North America	12	
Asia	5	
Other	5	
Total		360°

Now show the information by drawing:
a) a pie chart,
b) a bar graph.

 Draw your pie chart accurately.

Interpreting Tables, Graphs and Diagrams

Q1　Below is some data on the number of shell suits bought in Weirdyland since 1993. The table shows the number of shell suits bought by people who already own at least one shell suit, and by people who don't have a shell suit already.

Year	Number of shell suits bought by shell suit owners	Number of 'first' shell suits bought	Total shell suits bought	Number of shell suits thrown out
1993	339	57		27
1994	357	65		40
1995	389	82		63
1996	360	125		129
1997	279	140		160
1998	257	137		175
1999	241	135		135
2000	192	130		168
2001	179	122		170

a) Copy the table and complete the empty column to show the total number of shell suits bought in each year.

b) Plot **total shell suits bought** and **shell suits thrown out** as line graphs on the same axes.

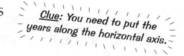

Clue: You need to put the years along the horizontal axis.

c) Comment on any trends you can see.

Q2　Here is some weather information from Wacky Island.

	Mon	Tues	Weds	Thurs	Fri	Sat	Sun
midday temperature (°C)	14	17	26	32	29	30	23
midnight temperature (°C)	10	7	12	17	15	15	13
rainfall (cm)	10	5	3	0	0	0	1

a) Plot a line graph of midday temperatures. Describe how the midday temperatures change over the week.

b) On the same graph plot the midnight temperatures. Describe how the midnight temperatures change over the week.

c) Describe how the rainfall changes over the week.

Graph announcement — practise graphs and get more marks...

Plotting a graph or drawing a table is sometimes easier than working out what it's actually saying. But with a wee bit of practice, even that can seem as easy as putting on a pair of fancy trousers.

Interpreting Results

Q1   Mr Dingle and Ms Fangle work in a travel agency.
In 2001, they sold the following numbers of holidays.

	Jan	Feb	Mar	Apr	May	Jun	Jul	Aug	Sep	Oct	Nov	Dec
Mr Dingle	40	60	84	11	23	49	79	60	62	61	59	52
Ms Fangle	47	67	48	51	53	57	63	68	69	72	51	53

a) Work out the mean, median and range of both salespeople.

b) Which salesperson is more consistent? Explain your reasoning.

c) The two salespeople want to convince their manager that they deserve a pay rise.
Which average, the **mean** or the **median**, do you think each of them should use to explain
how good they are?

d) Who do you think had the better year, and why?

Q2   Work out the **mode**, **mean**, **median** and **range** of these data sets.
Choose the 'best' average for each data set, and comment on your results.

a) Test scores: 20   20   25   26   29   31   32   33

b) Test scores: 10   18   20   25   30   30   30   31

c) Lottery winnings: £10   £10   £10   £10   £10   £10   £10   £25,000

d) TV prices: £315   £334   £180   £358   £180   £235   £270   £989

Q3   Duncan is a maths teacher who has a pet monkey. His monkey is
playing with a dice. He throws it 24 times and gets the following scores.

Score	1	2	3	4	5	6
Number of throws	4	3	5	3	3	6

Duncan's monkey thinks the results show that the dice is biased.

Duncan thinks he doesn't have enough information to know that yet.

Who is right?

This page will cause a range of emotions...

Working out an average isn't as simple as it sounds — after all, there are different kinds of average.
And the mean, median and mode might not turn out to be very similar at all. It's a right pain.

Probability 1

Q1   Match each event to its probability.

> impossible   unlikely   has an even chance   likely   certain

a) The Sun will rise tomorrow morning.

b) A card drawn from a pack will be red.

c) The next person you meet will be male.

d) It will rain slugs tonight.

e) It will snow next week.

f) You will live to be 203.

g) The first baby to be born next year will be a boy.

h) Someone will holiday on the Moon next year.

i) You will get cards on your birthday.

j) You will get a car for Christmas.

Q2   These two snack machines dish out random snacks when someone puts
money in. (The different types of snack are all equally likely to be given out.)
Which machine should the following people use?

a) Ophelia — she likes savoury snacks (e.g. nuts and crisps).

b) Hamlet — he likes chocolate best.

c) Macbeth — he hates boiled sweets.

Q3   The Lottery machine chooses each ball **totally at random**.
Ball number 7 has been drawn for four weeks running.

Beatrice thinks that the number 7 ball is likely to be drawn again this week.

Benedict thinks that the number 7 ball cannot be drawn five weeks in a row.

Who is right?

Probability II

Q1   Jason has these Scrabble tiles and he puts them in a bag.
He chooses one without looking.

What is the probability of getting:

a) a Y?   e) a letter from the first word?

b) an A?   f) a tile with a number 1?

c) an S?   g) a tile with a number 4?

d) a vowel?   h) a letter with 2 lines of symmetry?

Q2   The three witches have made a stew containing their
favourite pets. Macbeth takes one without looking.

What is the probability of him getting:

a) a slug?

b) a maggot?

c) a creature with legs?

d) not a snail?

e) a creature whose name begins with S?

Witches cauldron containing:
9 slugs
8 snails
6 maggots
5 spiders

Q3   Maximus Quartius Beranius drives up to a particular set of traffic lights in his
chariot. The probability of the lights being red is $\frac{3}{8}$, and the probability of
them being green is $\frac{1}{2}$. What is the probability of them being amber?

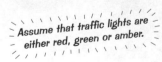

Assume that traffic lights are
either red, green or amber.

Q4   The weather centre says that the probability of it snowing one Christmas Day is 1 in 50.

a) Write this probability as a **fraction**, a **decimal** and a **percentage**.

b) What is the probability that it will **not** snow on that particular Christmas Day?

Probability — Recording Outcomes

Q1   Copy and complete this table to show all the possible outcomes when a coin and a dice are thrown.

	1	2	3	4	5	6
Head (H)	H1					
Tail (T)				T4		

What is the probability of getting:

a) a head and a 5?

b) a tail and a 2?

c) a head and an even number?

d) a prime number and a tail?

e) a number less than 3?

f) a number greater than 4 and a tail?

g) a factor of 6?

h) a head and a 7?

Q2   Malvolio has two dice. One has 6 faces numbered 0, 2, 4, 6, 8 and 10, while the other has 4 faces numbered 1, 3, 5 and 7. He plays two different games.

In the first he throws the two dice and adds the scores.
Copy and complete the probability diagram.

a) What is the probability of getting a score of 1?

b) What is the probability of getting a score of 5?

c) What are the most likely outcomes?

d) What is the probability of getting more than 9?

+	0	2	4	6	8	10
1						
3		5				
5						
7					15	

e) What is the probability of getting an even score?

Malvolio's second game involves throwing the two dice and finding the product of the scores. Copy and complete this table.

×	0	2	4	6	8	10
1						
3		6				
5						
7					56	

f) What is the probability of getting an even number?

g) What is the probability of getting 0?

h) What is the probability of getting less than 10?

i) What is the probability of getting a score that is a multiple of 8 and greater than zero?

Experimental and Theoretical Probability

Q1   Dogberry tossed a biased coin 100 times. He got 62 heads and 38 tails.

a) What was the probability of getting a head with his next thow, **based on this information**?

b) He tossed the coin a further 100 times and got 59 heads and 41 tails.
   Work out the probability of getting a tail on his next throw, using the data for **all 200 throws**.

c) Roughly how many heads and tails do you think he will get if he throws the coin 1000 times?

Q2   For homework, Ophelia, Juliet, Portia
      and Bernard are asked to toss a dice 120
      times and record their results in the table.

a) Who had a biased dice?

b) Who cheated and made up their results?

Explain your reasons.

	Ophelia	Juliet	Portia	Bernard
1	19	20	35	16
2	23	20	5	20
3	21	20	22	17
4	17	20	19	19
5	21	20	33	24
6	19	20	6	22

Q3   Below is some data from the National Lottery Draw.

Ball number	1	2	3	4	5	6	7	8	9	10
Frequency	89	79	74	75	80	82	76	85	80	87

Macduff says he will choose numbers 1 and 10 rather than numbers
3 and 4 next week, as 1 and 10 are more likely to be picked.

Is he correct?

IT ALMOST CERTAINLY
WON'T BE YOU.

This should probably be easy — in theory...

It's normal for <u>theoretical</u> results and <u>experimental</u> results to be slightly different. But if the
difference seems really big, then something might be wrong — maybe the coin or dice is biased.

Estimating Probabilities

Q1 Terry the dandy turtle opens a bag of 20 mixed sweets, and eats a chocolate, a toffee and two mints.

a) What is the smallest number of mints that the bag could have originally contained?

He then reads the label which says the bag originally contained 6 chocolates, 6 toffees and 8 mints.

b) How many of each sweet are left in the bag?

c) What is the probability of his next sweet being a toffee?

d) What is the probability of the next sweet being a mint?

e) Which sweet is he most likely to get next?

Q2 Devise an experiment to investigate the probability of getting 3 even numbers when you roll 3 dice.

Write all the possible outcomes and decide on the theoretical probability.

Q3 This is the menu for Fridays in the school canteen. Rowena wants to choose her meal randomly, so she's going to use a dice.

Hint: Devise some sort of shorthand to make this quicker, e.g. P for pork, Y for yoghurt etc.

a) How could Rowena use a dice to choose one random main course and one random dessert?

b) Write a list of all the possible meal combinations.

c) What is the probability of her having a cold main course?

d) What is the probability of having both meat and custard?

e) What is the probability of her **not** having to eat cook's lumpy gravy?

f) How many different meal options are there altogether if Rowena can also choose between juice or milk to drink?

g) Have you ever eaten a slug or a small insect that's been dead for a day or two?

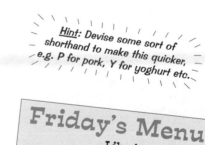

Friday's Menu

Like it or lump it

Main Course

burnt pork, gravy and soggy cabbage

soggy salad and cheese

fatty fish and chips

Dessert

apple and maggot pie and custard

yellow yoghurt

black bananas

Served with love, pride and a bit of slime

I estimate this will probably be quite dull...

Working out probabilities often comes down to making a list of all the possible outcomes in a situation. Fun it ain't, but you need to know what you're doing. A bit of practice is sure to help.

The Answers

Section One — Numbers and the Number System

Page 1

Q1 a) 5   6   7   8   9
b) 3.3   3.4   3.5   3.6   3.7
c) 5.42 5.43 5.44 5.45 5.46
d) 4.99 5.00 5.01 5.02 5.03
e) 4.1   4.0   3.9   3.8   3.7
f) 5.80 5.78 5.76 5.74 5.72

Q2 a) $430 \times 0.1 = 430 \div 10 = 43$
b) $673 \times 0.01 = 673 \div 100 = 6.73$
c) $8137 \times 0.001 = 8137 \div 1000 = 8.137$
d) $18430 \times 0.01 = 18430 \div 100 = 184.3$
e) $127 \times 0.1 = 127 \div 10 = 12.7$
f) $8 \times 0.01 = 8 \div 100 = 0.08$
g) $73 \times 0.001 = 73 \div 1000 = 0.073$
h) $2.3 \times 0.1 = 2.3 \div 10 = 0.23$

Q3 a) 7.73
b) 7.9
c) 0.655
d) 0.65
e) 1.39
f) 9.941
g) 6.278
h) 9.999

Q4 a) any number > 1, any number < 1
b) any number < 1, any number > 1

Page 2

Q1 a) 7.4   7.43
b) 9.8   9.83
c) 121.1   121.12
d) 345.7   345.68
e) 1.2   1.19
f) 2.3   2.30
g) 10.0   9.99
h) 5.0   5.00

Q2 a) 0.125
b) 0.0625
c) 0.1̇
d) 0.625
e) 0.4375
f) 0.6̇3̇
g) 0.3̇
h) 0.4̇5̇

Q3 a) One million one hundred and twenty-eight thousand (1 128 000); One hundred and nine thousand (109 000)
b) 2 090 000
c) 1 130 000
d) 100 000

Q4 a) 19000
b) 5900
c) 7490
d) 7500

Page 3

Q1 a) -9, -3, -1, 1, 6, 8
b) -3.3, -2.9, -0.5, 0, 0.4, 3.4
c) -312, -231, -213, -132, -123, -121
d) -0.312, -0.123, -0.101, 0.121, 0.123, 0.312

e) 120.21, 121.01, 121.02, 121.10, 121.12, 121.21
f) -79.39, -74.44, -74.411, -74.404, -74.4, -74.32

Q2 a) -5
b) -14
c) -9
d) 7
e) 13
f) -6
g) 0
h) 6

Q3

×	2	-3	-5	7	8	-11
1	2	-3	-5	7	8	-11
-4	-8	12	20	-28	-32	44
-5	-10	15	25	-35	-40	55
9	18	-27	-45	63	72	-99
-10	-20	30	50	-70	-80	110
6	12	-18	-30	42	48	-66

Q4

```
  30              -6             -10
 17  13         -1  -5         -9  -1
10  7  6        3  -4  -1      -6  -3  2
7  3  4  2      4  -1  -3  2   1  -7  4  -2
```

Page 4

Q1 a) 1, 2, 3, 4, 6, 12
b) 1, 2, 3, 4, 6, 8, 12, 16, 24, 48
c) 1, 3, 9, 27, 81
d) 1, 2, 3, 6, 7, 9, 14, 18, 21, 42, 63, 126
e) 1, 2, 4, 5, 8, 10, 20, 25, 40, 50, 100, 200
f) 1, 2, 5, 7, 10, 14, 25, 35, 50, 70, 175, 350
g) 1, 3, 9, 27
h) 1, 2, 3, 4, 6, 9, 12, 18, 36

Q2 a) $12 = 2^2 \times 3$
b) $48 = 2^4 \times 3$
c) $200 = 2^3 \times 5^2$
d) $350 = 2 \times 5^2 \times 7$

Q3 a) 6
b) 8
c) 5
d) 4
e) 11
f) 1

Q4 a) 54
b) 495
c) 4320
d) 36288
e) 690
f) 1855

Q5 a) 3
b) 5
c) 10
d) 15
e) 35
f) 70

Page 5

Q1 a) $10 \times 10 = 10^2 = 100$ = one hundred
b) $10 \times 10 \times 10 = 10^3 = 1000$ = one thousand
c) $10 \times 10 \times 10 \times 10 \times 10 = 10^5 = 100\,000$ = one hundred thousand
d) $10 \times 10 \times 10 \times 10 \times 10 \times 10 \times 10 = 10^7 = 10\,000\,000$ = ten million

e) $10 \times 10 \times 10 \times 10 = 10^4 = 10\,000$ = ten thousand
f) $10 \times 10 \times 10 \times 10 \times 10 \times 10 = 10^6 = 1\,000\,000$ = one million

Q2 a) $3^2 = 9$ therefore $\sqrt{9}$ = 3 or -3
b) $4^2 = 16$ therefore $\sqrt{16}$ = 4 or -4
c) $2^3 = 8$ therefore $\sqrt[3]{8}$ = 2
d) $8^2 = 64$ therefore $\sqrt{64}$ = 8 or -8
e) $10^2 = 100$ so $\sqrt{100}$ = 10 or -10

Q3 Number line showing values approx
a) 1.4
b) 5.5
c) 7.1
d) 7.7
e) 3.1
f) 9.7

Q4 a) 12.250
b) 0.281
c) 389.017
d) 2.569
e) 3.733
f) 1030.301
g) 0.990
h) 0.993

Page 6

Q1 a) 12 of the 24 squares should be shaded
b) 8 squares should be shaded
c) 4 squares should be shaded
d) 3 squares should be shaded
e) 9 squares should be shaded
f) 18 squares should be shaded

Q2 a) 1/4, 1/2, 3/4, 1 1/4, 9/2
b) 1/8, 1/4, 3/8, 5/8, 3/4
c) 1/7, 2/7, 4/7, 6/7, 12/7
d) 1/4, 3/8, 7/16, 1/2, 5/8
e) 1/10, 4/20 = 1/5, 3/10, 3/5
f) 3/20, 23/100, 13/50, 3/10, 12/25

Q3 a) 1/2
b) 3/20
c) 1/20
d) 3/10
e) 6
f) 6/11

Q4 1/2 left in fridge,
1/10 left for Chuck Norris.

Page 7

Q1 a) 3/4
b) 1 2/7
c) 2 1/3
d) 1 1/4
e) 5/8
f) 1/2
g) 17/21
h) 1/20

Q2 a) 5
b) 24
c) 16
d) 1/8
e) 1 1/8
f) 5/12
g) 10/21
h) 1 3/7

Q3 a) 1/8
b) 1/4

The Answers

c) 1
d) 2
e) 4
f) 2/5
g) 7 1/3
h) 9/28

Q4 a) 1 1/8 = 9/8
b) 3 3/4 = 15/4
c) 1 7/20 = 27/20
d) 1 1/4 = 10/8
e) 23/7 = 3 4/14
f) 9/5 = 27/15
g) 2 5/8 = 42/16
h) 5 1/2 = 44/8

Q5 7/24

Page 8

Q1 a) 60
b) £2.25
c) £100
d) 9 m
e) 332.5 kg
f) 8.5 l
g) 37.5 m
h) 108.48 kg

Q2

percentage	decimal fraction	fraction
50	0.5	1/2
25	0.25	1/4
20	0.2	1/5
10	0.1	1/10
5	0.05	1/20
16	0.16	4/25
36	0.36	9/25
84	0.84	21/25

Q3 a) 50% of 568 = 50/100 × 568
   = 0.5 × 568 = 1/2 × 568 = 284
b) 13.5
c) 930
d) 6.7
e) 39
f) 60
g) 27
h) 63

Q4 Yes, always true.

Page 9

Q1 a) 13.5 litres
b) 1350 litres
c) 2/9 gallons
d) 11 5/9 = 11.6 miles

Q2 a) 19p
b) 95p
c) 4/19

Q3 a) £1.60
b) £9.60
c) 6.25 m

Q4

Amount bought	Steps CD singles	Steps CD albums	Steps T-Shirts	H plastic doll
1	25p	17p	22p	13p
2	50p	34p	44p	26p
3	75p	51p	66p	39p
4	£1	68p	88p	52p
5	£1.25	85p	£1.10	65p
6	£1.50	£1.02	£1.32	78p

Page 10

Q1 2:3

Q2 25 girls

Q3 a) 800
b) 1/5

Q4 a) 5 : 3 : 2
b) 3/10
c) 4/5

Q5 15 barrows of grass, 5 of kitchen waste and 25 of toilet paper.

Q6 a) 2.5 km
b) 1 : 250 000
c) 2.4 cm

Q7 900 m

Section Two — Calculations

Page 11

Q1 a) 28
b) -24
c) 36
d) -6
e) -6
f) 2
g) 5
h) 1

Q2 a) 78
b) 561
c) 4375.8
d) 43.758
e) 5.61
f) 78
g) 280.5
h) 1122

Q3 a) Incorrect (should be 5488)
b) Correct
c) Correct
d) Incorrect (should be 1561)
e) Correct
f) Correct
g) Incorrect (should be 4.03125)
h) Incorrect (should be 2.775)

Q4 a) $32 \div 4 - 7 = 1$
b) $21 \times 3 + 46 = 109$
c) $(14 - 11) \times 4 = 12$
d) $(36 - 4) \div 2 = 16$

Page 12

Q1 a) no (ans = 6)
b) he has keyed "12 ÷ 4 × 0.5 ="
c) and d) key "12 ÷ 4 ÷ 0.5"
   OR key "12 ÷ (4 × 0.5)"
   OR key "4 × 0.5 ="
   then key "12 ÷ Ans ="

Q2 key "140 ÷ (7 + 13) ="
   OR key "7 + 13 ="
   then key "140 ÷ Ans ="

Q3 a) 0.7 + 5.2 − 2.1 = 3.8
b) 8.2 − 5.7 − -3 = 2.5 + 3 = 5.5
c) 23.7 − 2 × 2.4 = 23.7 − 4.8 = 18.9
d) 104 − 7 × -7.8 = 104 + 54.6 = 158.6
e) $\frac{12}{0.08} = 150$

f) $\frac{37 - 17}{-20} = \frac{20}{-20} = -1$
g) 3 × (4 − 2×0.35) = 3 × (4 − 0.7)
   = 3 × 3.3 = 9.9
h) $\frac{2 \times 0.16 - 2 \times 0.04}{0.62} = \frac{0.32 - 0.08}{0.62} = \frac{0.24}{0.62} = 0.387$

Q4 Possible answers: -16, -4, 8, 13, 16, 19, 40.

Page 13

Q1 a) 63
b) 43
c) 6.4
d) 1.7
e) 330
f) 583
g) 0.57
h) 1.129

Q2 a) 24
b) 2400
c) 240 000
d) 4
e) 400
f) 40 000
g) 64
h) 64 000

Q3 a) 76
b) 152
c) 56
d) 43
e) 603
f) 7740
g) 685
h) 66 330

Q4 a) 2 × 8   0.2 × 80
   0.02 × 800   20 × 0.8
b) 4 ×13   40 × 1.3
   0.4 × 130   0.04 × 1300
c) 0.7 × 1.1   7 × 0.11
   11 × 0.07   0.007 × 110
d) 127 × 0.07   12.7 × 0.7
   7 × 1.27   700 × 0.0127
e) 12 ÷ 4   120 ÷ 40
   1.2 ÷ 0.4   1200 ÷ 400
f) 8.7 ÷ 12.1   87 ÷ 121
   0.87 ÷ 1.21   0.087 ÷ 0.121

Page 14

Q1 a) 8
b) 64
c) 9
d) 5
e) 125
f) 3
g) 10
h) 8

Q2 a) 2, 3, 5 $2 \times 3 \times 5$
b) 2, 3 2×3^2
c) 2 2^6
d) 3, 13 3×13
e) 3, 5 $3^2 \times 5^2$
f) 2, 7 2×7^2
g) 2, 7 $2^2 \times 7^2$
h) 5, 7, 11 $5 \times 7 \times 11$

Q3 a) 10
b) 13
c) 12
d) 49
e) 3
f) 169

The Answers

g) 81
h) 25

Q4 a) 120 s
b) 7200 s
c) 35 days
d) 168 hours
e) Total number of hours = 14.5 = 870 minutes. Heart beats 60 times per minute, so would beat 870 × 60 = 52 200 times in 14.5 hours.

Page 15

Q1 a) 107
b) 680
c) 314
d) 7502
e) 836
f) 306
g) 6.16
h) 2847

Q2 a) 0.45   9/20
b) 0.55   11/20
c) 0.15   3/20
d) 1.5   1 1/2
e) 2.3   2 3/10
f) 0.05   1/20
g) 0.175 7/40
h) 0.005 1/200

Q3 3/4 = 75%
1.3 = 130%
0.07 = 7/100
12.5% = 1/8
4.3 = 430%
27/50 = 54%
0.001 = 0.1%
33 1/3% = 1/3

Q4 a) 10
b) 20
c) 100
d) 74
e) 1030
f) 0.06
g) -7
h) -340

Page 16

Q1 a) 4
b) 9
c) Scores of 7 the same on both, otherwise reversed.

Total of top faces	Score on Dice 2					
Score on Dice 1	1	2	3	4	5	6
1	2	3	4	5	6	7
2	3	4	5	6	7	8
3	4	5	6	7	8	9
4	5	6	7	8	9	10
5	6	7	8	9	10	11
6	7	8	9	10	11	12

Total of bottom faces	Score on Dice 2					
Score on Dice 1	1	2	3	4	5	6
1	12	11	10	9	8	7
2	11	10	9	8	7	6
3	10	9	8	7	6	5
4	9	8	7	6	5	4
5	8	7	6	5	4	3
6	7	6	5	4	3	2

Q2 12.5 Yes

Q3 £99 then £89.10

Q4 a) 8642
b) 1357
c) 7285

Q5 24963 (= 157 × 159)

Q6 120 (= -10 × -12)

Page 17

Q1 a) 7 × 4 = 28 or similar
b) 88 ÷ 4 = 22 or similar
c) 45 + 105 = 150 or 40 + 100 = 140 or similar
d) 1100 − 1000 = 100 or similar
e) 150 × 50 ÷ 10 = 750 or similar
f) 30 × 80 ÷ 0.3 = 8000 or similar

Q2 a) 29.078
b) 5499
c) 307.23
d) 0.64837
e) 5300
f) 104.04

Q3 30 kg

Q4 32 cm × 38 cm

Q5 Pupil's own reasonable estimations, e.g. toilet flushed 15 times a day, 7 days a week...
so toilet flushed 15 × 7 = 105 times a week.
2 gallons used each time, so 210 gallons used per week.
17 houses in street, using 210 gallons per week...
so 17 × 210 = 3570 gallons used by my street each week.

Q6 Pupil's own reasonable estimations.

Page 18

Q1 a) 158.3
b) 70.8
c) 256.41
d) 1210.146
e) 21.5
f) 204.03
g) 66.241
h) 0.831

Q2 a) 2021
b) 15730
c) 79.81
d) 53.75
e) 10.22
f) 13.133
g) 5289
h) 25.9896

Q3 a) 20.097
b) 2009.7
c) 200.97
d) 2009.7
e) 200.97
f) 200.97
g) 200.97
h) 2.0097

Q4 3.1 × 4.7; 31 × 47 ÷ 100; (3 × 4.7) + (0.1 × 4.7)
9.9 × 63; 99 × 63 ÷ 10; (63 × 10) − (63 × 0.1)
0.021 × 463; 21 × 463 ÷ 1000; (2 × 4.63) + 0.463
2.1 × 46.3; 21 × 463 ÷ 100; (2 × 46.3) + 4.63
31 × 0.047; 31 × 47 ÷ 1000; (3 × 0.47) + 0.047
210 × 46.3; 21 × 463; (2 × 4630) + 463

Page 19

Q1 a) 17
b) 31
c) 52
d) 23
e) 55
f) 12
g) 34
h) 0.13

Q2 a) 246 rem 1
b) 45 rem 10
c) 5 rem 35
d) 76 rem 11
e) 42 rem 14
f) 4 rem 10
g) 21 rem 1
h) 51 rem 1

Q3 a) 31
b) 457
c) 13
d) 256
e) 6
f) 27

Q4 £192.86 : £964.29 : £1542.86
Rounding errors mean the three don't add up to exactly £2700.

Page 20

Q1 a) 31/56
b) 61/117
c) 1 50/99
d) 1 36/175
e) 1 1/3
f) 21/40
g) 15 3/16
h) 3 1/3

Q2 a) 7 7/60 min = 7 min 7 s
b) 6 19/60 min = 6 min 19 s
c) 11 7/30 min = 11 min 14 s
d) 5 3/20 h = 5 h 9 min
e) 1 3/10 h = 1 h 18 min
f) 8/15 h = 32 min
g) 8 9/20 h = 8 h 27 min
h) 12 3/4 min = 12 min 45 s

Q3 a) 0.5
b) 0.75
c) 0.375
d) 0.1875
e) 0.4375
f) 0.036
g) 1.0667 (4 dp)
h) 7.14 (2dp)

Q4 a) 0.6
b) 6.5
c) 7.416 (3dp)
d) 4.290 (3dp)
e) 7.2
f) 48
g) 676
h) 216

The Answers

Page 21

Q1 a) 238.2
   b) 86.14
   c) 0.889
   d) 8.83
   e) 2.80
   f) 1079

Q2 a) The inverse of add is **subtract**.
   b) The inverse of divide is **multiply**.
   c) The inverse of multiply is **divide**.
   d) The inverse of subtract is **add**.
   e) The inverse of square is **square root**.
   f) The inverse of halve is **double**.
   g) The inverse of square root is **square**.
   h) The inverse of cube is **cube root**.

Q3 a) $75 - 7.8$ or $75 - 67.2$
   b) $0.36 + 0.87$ or $1.23 - 0.36$
   c) $-1 + 5$ or $4 - -1$
   d) $17.68 \div 5.2$ or $17.68 \div 3.4$
   e) $-65.8 \div -7$ or $-65.8 \div 9.4$
   f) $\sqrt{10.24}$
   g) $\sqrt[3]{226.981}$
   h) 1.077×7.8 and $8.4 \div 1.077$

Section Three — Solving Problems

Page 22

Q1 a) £20
   b) £35
   c) Shop B will be cheaper — the electric toenail clippers are £28 in both shops after reduction, but the Afro wigs work out cheaper in shop B (£28 compared to £32 in shop A).

Q2 The 7th day.

Q3 a) 2 : 3 : 5
   b) Newt eyes 4 : 6 : 10
     Worms 2 : 3 : 5
     Bat wings 6 : 9 : 15
     Vorbie Villiams CDs 4 : 6 : 10
   c) Heather — 7 CDs
     Chrissy — 13 CDs

Page 23

Q1 Many possible answers e.g. $\frac{5}{8}$, $\frac{9}{16}$, $\frac{17}{32}$.

Q2 a) 267 and 268
   b) 27 and 28
   c) 57, 58, 59
   d) 98, 100, 102, 104
   e) No because odd + even = odd
   f) Yes, odd + even + odd = even but even + odd + even = odd, so it only works if the first no. is odd.

Q3 2 (the last digit alternates 8, 4, 2, 6...)

Q4 $x = 7$ cm, Area is 140 cm²

Q5 Each side = 7 m, volume is 343 m³

Q6 a) 11, 13 ; 41 ; $2n + 1$
   b) 52, 59 ; 157 ; $7n + 17$
   c) 34, 29 ; -41 ; $59 - 5n$
   d) -2, 0 ; 28 ; $2n - 12$

Q7 a) $10x + 15$; $12x - 11$
   b) 13

Page 24

Q1 Forward 12 m, turn 20° anticlockwise, forward 8 m, turn 115° clockwise, forward 4 m, turn 80° anticlockwise, forward 7 m, turn 100° anticlockwise, forward 5 m, turn 90° clockwise, forward 14 m, turn 60° anticlockwise, forward 1 m, turn 90° clockwise, forward 9 m.

Q2 a)

Slice parallel to base (horizontally).

   b)

E.g. slice through the top point.

   c)

E.g. slice through a corner point at an angle to the horizontal (as shown).

   d)

E.g. slice at an angle to the horizontal so that the plane cuts through 4 edges (as shown).

Shapes you can make by slicing a cone: circle, ellipse, triangle (and parabola)

Q3 a) (0, 3)
   b) (0, 6)
   c) (3, 6)
   d) (1.5, 1.5)

Q4 192 cubes

Q5 a) 24 miles
   b) 8 miles
   c) 20 miles

Page 25

Q1 a)

dice	1	2	3	4	5	6
winnings	-£1	£2	-£3	£2	-£5	£2

   b) 10 of each
   c) -£30
   d) yes
   e) not a good idea: profits = losses

Q2 a) 4/10 = 2/5
   b) 5/7
   c) 2/8 = 1/4
   d) 3/9 = 1/3

Q3 123, 124, 132, 134, 142, 143
   213, 214, 231, 234, 241, 243
   312, 314, 321, 324, 341, 342
   412, 413, 421, 423, 431, 432

   a) 6/24 = 1/4
   b) 12/24 = 1/2
   c) 6/24 = 1/4
   d) 12/24 = 1/2
   e) 6/24 = 1/4

Page 26

Q1 a) £7
   b) £9.40 (accept £0.10 either side)
   c) 3.5 kg
   d) £2. You can't send a 0 kg parcel. This £2 represents the standing/minimum charge for sending a parcel.

Q2 a)

Witches' Favourite Spells

   b)

   c) 17.1% (1dp)

Page 27

Q1 a) 63.5 cm (accept 63.49 cm but discuss upper bounds)
   b) 62.5 cm
   c) 12.5 cm
   d) 11.5 cm
   e) 52 cm, 50 cm

Q2 a) 56.25 cm²
   b) 16 cm²

Q3 Other totals are: 30, 42, 56, 100;
   nth total = $n(n + 1)$

Q4 Totals are: 1, 4, 9, 16, 25, 36, 49, 100
   nth total = n^2

Page 28

Q1 a) $12^2 = 144$; $18^2 = 324$
   b) $16^3 = 4096$
   c) 2, 3, 7, 8
   d) they all occur
   e) 9

Q2 a) 40 pages (including front and back)
   b) Sheet 1 has 1, 40 and 2, 39
     Sheet 2 has 3, 38 and 4, 37
     Sheet 3 has 5, 36 and 6, 35
     Sheet 4 has 7, 34 and 8, 33 etc...

Q3 a) 78 gifts
   b) 364 gifts
   c) Crying Argies (4 × 9 days = 36)

The Answers

Page 29

Q1　a)　$n + (n + 1) = 2n + 1 = $ odd
　　b)　$n + (n + 1) + (n + 2)$
　　　　$= 3n + 3 = $ odd or even
　　　　$n + (n + 1) + (n + 2) + (n + 3)$
　　　　$= 4n + 6 = $ even
　　c)　$n + (n + 1) + (n + 2) + (n + 3) + (n + 4) = 5n + 10 = 5(n + 2)$, and so is divisible by 5.
　　d)　Three consecutive numbers are divisible by 3; seven consecutive numbers are divisible by 7; nine consecutive numbers are divisible by 9 — works for all odd numbers.

Q2　a)　14 cm × 14 cm × 3 cm
　　b)　2 cm × 2 cm × 9 cm
　　c)　No — biggest surface area has smallest corners removed,
　　　　i.e. 18 cm × 18 cm × 1 cm

Q3　Brutus

Q4　a)　2 lb 8 oz of potatoes, 5 lb of cabbage, 25 eggs, 1 lb 14 oz of cheese.
　　b)　6.4 oz of potatoes, 12.8 oz of cabbage, 4 eggs, 4.8 oz of cheese.
　　c)　(Approximately) 230 g of potatoes, 450 g of cabbage, 5 eggs, 170 g of cheese.

Page 30

Q1　a)　23 × 35 = 805; 33 × 25 = 825
　　b)　20
　　c)　all 20
　　d)　still 20
　　e)　difference = (height of rectangle − 1) × (width of rectangle − 1) × 10

Q2　a)　Yes
　　b)　Yes (cut off a corner)
　　c)　Yes (cut through the cube at an angle)
　　d)　Yes (cut the cube at a funny angle)
　　e)　Yes
　　f)　Yes

Section Four — Algebra

Page 31

Q1　a)　$4h$
　　b)　g
　　c)　$3f$
　　d)　$8e$
　　e)　$2cd$
　　f)　$5b + 5c$
　　g)　$3b$
　　h)　$5a/z$

Q2　a)　$C = 24x$
　　b)　$C = 23k$
　　c)　$C = kx$
　　d)　$C = kx/100$
　　e)　$N = 24/6 = 4$
　　f)　$N = 24/p$
　　g)　$N = q/6$
　　h)　$N = q/p$

Q3　$p + p = 2p$
　　$a - b + a = 2a - b$
　　$r + s - r = s$
　　$(t + t) \div 4u = t/2u$
　　$v + 2 + v - 5 = 2v - 3$
　　$a \times b = ba$
　　$1/2 \times w \times x = wx/2$
　　$3 + y - 7 - y + 4 = 0$

Page 32

Q1　a)　18, 24
　　b)　4, 2
　　c)　6.5, 4
　　d)　1, 3
　　e)　26, 36
　　f)　1, 49
　　g)　3, 27
　　h)　31, 15

Q2　a)　a^2
　　b)　b^3
　　c)　c^4
　　d)　a^2b
　　e)　d^2f^2
　　f)　g^4
　　g)　h^2g^2
　　h)　k^4

Q3　a)　z
　　b)　y^3
　　c)　x^4
　　d)　$2k$
　　e)　$5m$
　　f)　$2n^5$
　　g)　1
　　h)　1

Q4　a)　a^3
　　b)　b^3c^2
　　c)　$2d^2e^3$
　　d)　$9f^2$
　　e)　$125g^3$
　　f)　h^3
　　g)　$2k^2$
　　h)　$10k$

Page 33

Q1　a)　$8.1 - 4.4 = 3.7, 4.4 + 3.7 = 8.1$
　　b)　$16.9 - 9.8 = 7.1, 16.9 - 7.1 = 9.8$
　　c)　$5 - b = a, 5 - a = b$
　　d)　$c - k = d, k + d = c$
　　e)　$h - f = e, h - e = f$
　　f)　$h - f = 3e, h - 3e = f$
　　g)　$n + 4m = 7k, 7k - n = 4m$
　　h)　$r - q = p^2, r - p^2 = q$

Q2　a)　$18.87 \div 3.7 = 5.1,$
　　　　$18.87 \div 5.1 = 3.7$
　　b)　$13.8 \div 2.3 = 6, 2.3 \times 6 = 13.8$
　　c)　$a = 6/b, b = 6/a$
　　d)　$h = k/j, j = k/h$
　　e)　$m/4 = n, m = 4n$
　　f)　$p = r/q, q = r/p$
　　g)　$xy/a = z, xy = az$ (or other correct)
　　h)　$b = d/(c + 4), c + 4 = d/b$

Q3　a)　$m = C/3$
　　b)　$n = D - 1$
　　c)　$p = E + 7$
　　d)　$q = 6F$
　　e)　$r = (G - 1)/2$
　　f)　$s = (H + 2)/3$
　　g)　$t = (J - 7)/2$
　　h)　$u = K - 21$

Page 34

Q1　a)　$2y + 2z$ or $2(y + z)$
　　b)　$8a$
　　c)　$6w - 2v$
　　d)　$5c - 5d$ or $5(c - d)$
　　e)　$2u - 2t + 10$ or $2(u - t + 5)$
　　f)　$4f - 2g + 1$
　　g)　$5r - 4s - 3$

　　h)　$-h - 3j - 1$

Q2　a)　$3p + 2q$
　　b)　$2r + 7s$
　　c)　$7t - u$
　　d)　$3v + 7w - 7x$
　　e)　$8a + 4b + 3c$
　　f)　$-4c - 4d$
　　g)　$6e + 27$
　　h)　$3 - f$

Q3　a)　$3a$
　　b)　$2b + 3$
　　c)　$4d + 4$
　　d)　$4c + 9$
　　e)　$7e + 4$

Q4　a)　$8(ef + 4)$
　　b)　$(h + j)^2 - k$
　　c)　$p(2m - n) + q$

Page 35

Q1　$2(a + b) = 2a + 2b$
　　　　$= 4a - (2a - 2b)$
　　$6a + 2b = 0.5(12a + 4b)$
　　　　$= 2(b + 3) - 6(1 - a)$
　　$a + 10b + 5$
　　　　$= 3a + 4b + 6(b + 1) - 2a - 1$
　　　　$= a + 5(2b + 1)$
　　$7 - 3a + 4b$
　　　　$= 3(2 - a) + 4(b + 1) - 3$
　　　　$= 2(4 + 2b) + 5 - 3(a + 2)$

Q2　1 and 8
　　2 and 7
　　3 and 6
　　4 and 10
　　5 and 9

Page 36

Q1　a)　$z = 4$
　　b)　$y = 11$
　　c)　$x = 4$
　　d)　$w = 5$
　　e)　$v = 12$
　　f)　$u = 36$
　　g)　$t = 1.6$
　　h)　$t = 0.625$

Q2　a)　$s = 2$
　　b)　$r = 3$
　　c)　$q = 19$
　　d)　$p = 28$
　　e)　$n = 2$
　　f)　$m = 12$
　　g)　$k = 2$
　　h)　$j = 6$

Q3　a)　$a = 4$
　　b)　$b = 9$
　　c)　$c = 2$
　　d)　$d = 0$
　　e)　$e = 4$
　　f)　$f = 1$
　　g)　$g = 1$
　　h)　$h = 2$

Q4　a)　Delilah $k + 4$ and Cleopatra $3k$
　　b)　$5k + 4$
　　c)　$5k + 4 = 229$
　　d)　Delilah 49, Desdemona 45, Cleopatra 135

The Answers

Page 37

Q1
a) $z = 4$
b) $y = 4$
c) $x = 1$
d) $v = 6$
e) $u = 14$
f) $t = 0$
g) $s = 1.5$
h) $q = -1$

Q2
A and D
B and H
C and E
F and G

Q3
a) $a = 4$ (so $a = g$)
b) $b = 5$ (so $b = d$)
c) $c = 3$ (so $c = h$)
d) $d = 5$ (so $d = b$)
e) $e = 8$ (so $e = f$)
f) $f = 8$ (so $f = e$)
g) $g = 4$ (so $g = a$)
h) $h = 3$ (so $h = c$)

Page 38

Q1
a) $a = 3$
b) $b = 4$
c) $c = 6$
d) $a = 4$
e) $b = 1$
f) $c = 7$
g) $a = 2$
h) $b = 3$

Q2
a) Jane: $3x + 2$, Tarzan: $x + 16$
b) $3x + 2 = x + 16$
c) $x = 7$, they both have 23 bananas

Q3
a) Desdemona: $3a - 10$
Portia: $a + 10$
b) $3a - 10 = a + 10$
$a = 10$
She had 30 figs to start with.

Q4
a) $3y + 2 = 2y + 8$
b) $y = 6$, so there are 6 Kat-Kits in a multipack.

Page 39

Q1
a) 160 euros
b) 1.6 euros
c) $e = 1.6p$
d) £31.25
e) 140
f) 1.4
g) $d = 1.4p$
h) £35.71

Q2
a) 660, 990, 1320, 1980, 2640
b) $d = 330t$
c)

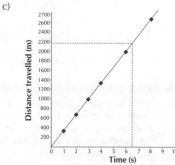

d) From graph, answer is about 2150 m
e) $330 \times 3.4 \div 2 = 560$ m (to 2 s.f.)

Page 40

Q1
a) 9
b) 4
c) 0
d) 14
e) 13
f) 1
g) 17
h) -5

Q2
a) 3
b) -1
c) 0
d) 1/2
e) 5/7
f) -1/3

Q3
a) 0
b) -1/2 *or* -0.5
c) -3/5 *or* -0.6
d) -5
e) 2/5 *or* 0.4
f) -10/19 *or* -0.53 (to 2 d.p.)

Q4
a) 120
b) 325
c) 205
d) 1297215

Page 41

Q1
a) 6 cm²
b) $A = pq/2$
c) 84 cm²
d) $S = pq + rs + qs + ps$
or $S = pq + s(p + q + r)$
e) 36 cm³
f) $V = pqs/2$
g) 810 cm², 397.5 cm³

Q2
a) $a = 3b; a = 300$
b) $a = 2b + 3; a = 203$
c) $a = b + 20; a = 120$
d) $b - 5 = a + 5; a = 90$
e) $a/2 + 2b = 3a; a = 80$

Page 42

Q1

	a)	b)	c)	d)	e)
Flow Chart 1	-2	0	2	16	-24
Flow Chart 2	4	9	16	121	81
Flow Chart 3	-9	-2	17	990	-1010

Q2
a) 1/2, 2/3, 3/4, 4/5 etc.
b) getting nearer to 1
c) 10/11 = 0.90909...
100/101 = 0.990099...
d) answer almost 1

Page 43

Q1
a) Add 2; 18, 20, 22
b) Divide by 2; 28, 14, 7
c) Add 3; 15, 18, 21
d) Multiply by 2; 48, 96, 192
e) Subtract 2; 0, -2, -4
f) Add 3; -1, 2, 5
g) Subtract 3; -17, -20, -23
h) Squares of 1, 2, 3 etc.; 25, 36, 49

Q2
a) 5, 7, 11, 19
b) 3, 3, 3, 3
c) -3, -9, -21, -45
d) 197, 391, 779, 1555
e) -43, -89, -181, -365
f) -2, -7, -17, -37
g) -2.5, -8, -19, -41
h) 3.2, 3.4, 3.8, 4.6

Q3
a) 2, 6, 10, 38, 98
b) 9, 8, 7, 0, -15
c) 5, 12, 19, 68, 173
d) 98, 96, 94, 80, 50
e) -7, -2, 3, 38, 113
f) 1, 4, 9, 100, 625
g) 3.5, 4, 4.5, 8, 15.5
h) 3, 8, 15, 120, 675

Q4
a) 1, 3, 5, 7 and 3, 5, 7, 9
Both are sequences of odd numbers, but A starts at 1 while B starts at 3.
b) $2n + 21$
c) $2n + 40$

Page 44

Q1
a)

term number	1	2	3	4	5	6	7	8
number of dots	1	3	5	7	9	11	13	15

b) 19, 59
c) $2n - 1$

Q2
a)

pattern number	1	2	3	4	5	6	7	8
number of squares	6	9	12	15	18	21	24	27

b) 33, 93
c) $3n + 3$

Q3
a)

pattern number	1	2	3	4	5	6	7	8
number of dark	1	2	3	4	5	6	7	8
number of light	8	10	12	14	16	18	20	22

b) 50 dark and 106 light
c) n dark, $2n + 6$ light
d) $n + 2n + 6 = 3n + 6 = 3(n + 2)$.
This is the area of a rectangle 3 by ($n + 2$).

Page 45

Q1
a)

$x \rightarrow$	$3x + 2$
0	2
1	5
2	8
3	11
4	14
5	17
6	20

b)

$x \rightarrow$	$x + 5$
-3	2
-2	3
-1	4
0	5
1	6
2	7
3	8

c)

$x \rightarrow$	$2x - 5$
0	-5
1	-3
2	-1
3	1
4	3
5	5
6	7

d)

$x \rightarrow$	$6 - 1/2x$
0	6
1	5.5
2	5
3	4.5
4	4
5	3.5
6	3

The Answers

e)

x →	4 – x
0	4
1	3
2	2
3	1
4	0
5	-1
6	-2

f)

x →	x/4 + 1
-3	1/4
-2	1/2
-1	3/4
0	1
1	1 1/4
2	1 1/2
3	1 3/4

a)

b)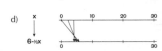

c)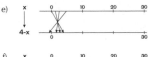

d)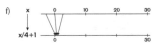

e)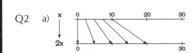

f)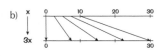

d) and e) are the only mappings in which the arrows cross over.

Q2 a)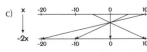

b)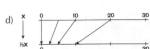

c)

d)

(or similar correct diagrams)

Page 46

Q1 ×2, +4
+2, ×2

Q2 a) $x \rightarrow (x + 2) \times 2$ OR $x \rightarrow 2x + 4$
b) $x \rightarrow (x – 6) \div 3$ OR $x \rightarrow (x \div 3) – 2$
c) $x \rightarrow (x \div 2) + 4$
OR $x \rightarrow (x + 8) \div 2$
d) $x \rightarrow (x – 20) \div 5$
OR $x \rightarrow (x \div 5) – 4$

Q3 a) $x \rightarrow 2x + 6$
b) $x \rightarrow 3x + 3$
c) $x \rightarrow 2x + 16$
d) $x \rightarrow 3x + 8$

Q4 a) $x \rightarrow 1/2x$
b) $x \rightarrow 1/4x$
c) $x \rightarrow 2x$
d) $x \rightarrow x – 34$
e) $x \rightarrow x + 107$
f) $x \rightarrow (x – 3)/2$
g) $x \rightarrow x/3 – 3$
h) $x \rightarrow 3(x – 4)$

Page 47

Q1

x	-3	-2	-1	0	1	2	3
y = 2x – 4	-10	-8	-6	-4	-2	0	2

a), b) and e)

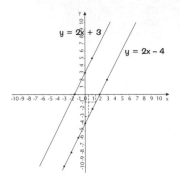

c) -1
d) 0.5
f) (0, -4) (0, 3)
g) Both lines have a gradient of 2.

Q2 a)

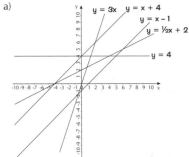

b) $y = x + 4$; $y = x – 1$
c) $y = x + 4$; $y = \frac{1}{2}x + 2$
d) Any one of (2, 6), (-0.5, -1.5), (0.8, 2.4), (0, 4), (1.33, 4), (4, 4), (5, 4), (6, 5).
e) Yes. The number in front of the x is the gradient of the line (when the equation is written in the form $y = mx + c$). The lines are parallel when the gradients are the same, so just look for 2 equations with the same number in front of x.

Q3 a) $x = 2$
b) $y = x$
c) $y = 0$
d) $y = 2x$

Page 48

Q1 a) $y = 2x – 1$
b) $y = 3/2x$
c) $y = x$
d) $y = x – 1$
e) $y = 1/4x + 1$
f) $y = 2 – x$

Q2

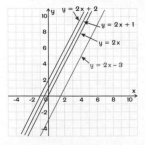

a) Each line has a gradient of 2.
b) The number term in the equation is the same as the y-intercept.
c) The new lines should be parallel to the other lines (i.e. have a gradient of 2) and intercept the y-axis at (0, 5) and (0, -½) respectively.

Q3

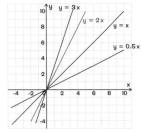

a) The gradients are 1, 2, 3, 0.5 respectively. The gradient of each line is the same as the number in front of the x in the equation.
b) All lines pass through the origin.
c) Line $y = 4x$ should have a gradient of 4 and pass through the origin.
Line $y = 1/4x$ should have a gradient of 1/4 and pass through the origin.

Q4 a) Line should have a gradient of 1 and intercept the y-axis at (0, 3).
b) Line should have a gradient of 2 and intercept the y-axis at (0, -4).
c) Line should have a gradient of ½ and intercept the y-axis at (0, 3).
d) Line should have a gradient of 6 and intercept the y-axis at (0, 1)

Page 49

Q1 a)

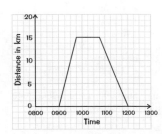

b) 20 km/h (or 0.33 km/min)
c) 12 km/h (or 0.2 km/min)

Q2 1 → A, 2 → D, 3 → B, 4 → C

Page 50

Q1 a) This graph shows the motion of a football being propelled into the air from an initial height of 0.5 m until it hits the ground. It could be the motion of the ball after a header or volley.

The Answers

b) The graph could represent the motion of a tennis ball after being hit by one player (from a height of 1 m) and then being volleyed by the other player from the same height before falling to the ground.

c) The graph shows a car accelerating jerkily to about 15 mph, then slowing steadily to a halt. The car then accelerates again up to a speed of 30 mph, which is maintained for a period of time, before it slows again to a halt. The wiggles in the car's acceleration could be the driver changing the pressure on the accelerator, applying the brakes or changing gear.

d) The graph shows a train accelerating to about 60 mph, maintaining its speed, then slowing to a halt. The train then accelerates again to about 100 mph and maintains this speed.
It then slows again to a stop.

e) The climber climbs upwards at a similar rate for most of the climb, except at about a third of the way up, where he stays at the same height. He could be resting at this point.

Q2 a) £20
b) £27

c)
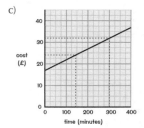

d) about £24
e) about 300 min

Q3
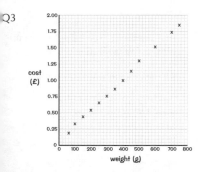

Section Five — Shape, Space and Measures

Page 51

Q1 BAC = 38°   BCD = 118°
CBD = 13°   FGE = HGI = 80°
EGH = 100°   GHI = 58°
EFG = 68°   JMK = 30°
LMK = 22°

Q2 a = 56°   *angles on a straight line: 180 − 124*
b = 56°   *same as opposite (a)*
c = 124° *same as opposite (124)*
d = 73°   *same as parallel angle e*
          e is same as opposite 73

e = 73°   *same as opposite 73*
f = 107°   *180 − 73 = 107*
g = 70°   *180 − 110 = 70*
h = 110°   *same as alternate 110*
j = 108°   *same as l + 80 = 108*
k = 72°   *180 − 108 = 72*
l = 28°   *180 − (72 + 80) = 28*
m = 80°   *same as alternate (80°)*
n = 100°   *180 − 80*

Q3 a = 35°   *same as opposite*
b = 70°   *same as alternate (70)*
c = 75°   *180 − 35 − 70 = 75*
d = 120°   *180 − (30 + 30) = 120*
e = 70°   *180 − (30 + 80) = 70*
f = 77°   *360 − (110 + 82 + 91) = 77*
g = 38°   *180 − 126 = 54*
          180 − 54 − 88 = 38
h = 142°   *360 − (36 + 40) = 284*
          284 ÷ 2 = 142

Page 52

Q1 pupil's own correct diagrams

Q2 A, B, C, D, E, H

Q3 a) 2 different isosceles triangles
b) a rectangle

Q4 a) angles 60°, 90°, 30°
b) angles 70°, 90°, 20°
c) angles 10°, 80°, 90°
d) angles 45°, 45°, 90°. It's a similar triangle to the original one.

Q5 a) squares
b) Yes e.g. "stair" shape

Page 53

Q1 *square:*   4 right angles
                4 equal sides
                diagonals equal in length
                diagonals intersect at 90°
                2 pairs of parallel sides
rectangle: 4 right angles
                2 opposite pairs of equal sides
                diagonals equal in length
                2 pairs of parallel sides
parallelogram: 2 pairs of equal angles
                2 opposite pairs of equal sides
                2 pairs of parallel sides
rhombus: 2 pairs of equal angles
                4 equal sides
                diagonals equal in length
                diagonals intersect at 90°
                2 pairs of parallel sides
kite: just 1 pair of equal angles
                2 adjacent pairs of equal sides
                diagonals intersect at 90°
trapezium: only 1 pair of parallel sides

Q2 40°, 40°, 100° or 40°, 70°, 70°

Q3 c) both angles are the same (about 41°)
d) rhombus
e) 114°, 24°

Page 54

Q1 pairs: A & I,   B & L,   C & K,
            D & F,   E & H,   G & J

Q2 congruent a) d)
not congruent b) c) e)

Page 55

Q1
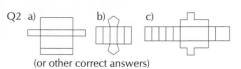

3D					
name	cube	cuboid	triangular prism	square-based pyramid	cylinder
net					
faces	6	6	5	5	3
edges	12	12	9	8	2
vertices	8	8	6	5	0

Q2 a)   b)   c)
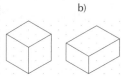
(or other correct answers)

Q3 a)   A: i) 3   ii) 5
        B: i) 3   ii) 6
        C: i) 6   ii) 5
        D: i) 3   ii) 4
b) C is the proper dice

Page 56

Q1 a)   b)
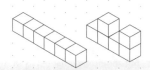

c) answer can be any two shapes made of 6 cubic bricks. e.g.

Q2 a)
b)
c)

Q3 a)   b)   c)   d)

Page 57

Q1 a) translation
b) reflection in vertical axis
c) rotation 90° anticlockwise
d) reflection in vertical axis then horizontal axis

Q2 E.g.
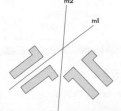

The Answers

Q3 a) A, B, C, D, E, K, M, T, U, V, W, Y
   b) H, I, O, X
   c) H, I, N, O, S, X, Z
   d) H, I, O, X
   e) F, G, J, L, P, Q, R

Page 58

Q1

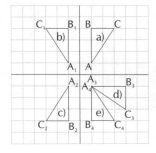

Q2

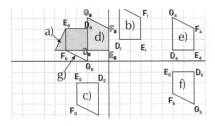

Q3 a) 180° rotation around (0,0)
   b) e.g. Reflect in x, reflect in y.

Page 59

Q1 a) 2
   b) 0.5
   c) 4

Q2 a) Not enough room for a scale answer —
       but should be enlarged as shown.

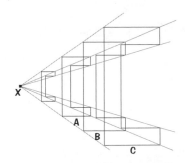

Q3 a) A': (2, 2)   B': (4, 2)   C': (2, 6)
   b) A'': (-1, 1)   B'': (1, -1)   C'': (-1, 3)
   c) A''': (1, 1)   B''': (3, 1)   C''': (1, 5)
   d) E.g. scale factor 4, centre 1, 4.

Page 60

Q1 a) Picture should be drawn to scale.
   b) Yes, there is 1.5 m of wall
   c) 1.5 m × 75 cm

Q2 45000 cm = 450 m

Q3 a) 1 900 000 cm
   b) 9.5 : 1 900 000
   c) 1 cm represents 2 km, 1 : 200 000
   d) 16 km

Page 61

Q1 MATHS IS COOL

Q2 a) (5, 3)
   b) (-1, 0)
   c) (3, 3)
   d) (-1, -1)
   e) (6, 2.5)
   f) (0, 0)
   g) (2, 0.5)
   h) (-2.5, 1.5)

Q3 b) E.g. could use the rectangle with
       corners at (1, 1), (4, 1), (4, 3) and (1, 3),
       then the diagonals intersect at the centre
       of the rectangle, i.e. (2½, 2).
   c) The diagonals intersect at their
       midpoints, so take two opposite
       corners of your rectangle and find the
       average of their x-coordinates and the
       y-coordinates.

Page 62

Q1,2,3,4   pupil's own drawings.

Q2 TUV and WXY are congruent

Q5 The drawing should show a perpendicular
    bisector.

Q6 point is where perpendicular bisectors of
    DE, DF and EF all cross.

Page 63

Q1

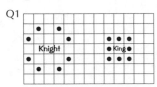

Q2 a), b), c), d), e), f)

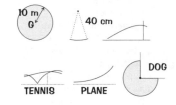

Q3 a) Students should use their own scale to
       draw the perpendicular bisector of the
       line segment

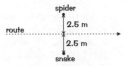

   b) The route should show a perpendicular
       bisector of the line at the midpoint, and
       should be drawn to scale.

Q4 see below for one possible route

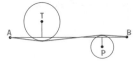

Page 64

Q1 a) gram, ounce
   b) metre, centimetre, foot, yard, inch
   c) metre, yard (or foot)
   d) hectare, acre
   e) kilometre, mile
   f) centimetre, inch
   g) kilogram, pound
   h) litre, gallon
   i) centilitre, pint or litre

Q2 a) 4500 g = 4.5 kg
   b) 7.75m = 775 cm
   c) 7.75m =7750 mm
   d) 8435m =8.435 km
   e) 7tonnes = 7000 kg
   f) 7 tonnes = 7 000 000 g
   g) 6.3 litres = 6300 ml
   h) 800ml = 0.8 litres
   i) 6cm = 60 mm
   j) 4.2 ha = 42000 m²

Q3 a) 00:00 5th Feb 2003
   b) 15:00 6th Jan 2003
   c) 12:00 30th Dec 2003
   d) (6d 22hr 40 min) 22:40 7th Jan 2003
   e) (16min 40 sec) 23:43:20 31st Dec 2002
   f) 12:30 3rd Feb 2135

Page 65

Q1 a) 090°
   b) 180°
   c) 000°
   d) 270°
   e) 135°
   f) 045°
   g) 202.5°
   h) 225°
   i) 022.5°
   j) 315°

Q2 a) - f)

Ulsta 7.6 cm
Fetlar
Papa Stour 7 cm
10.4 cm
Foula 9.8 cm
1.6 cm
Noss
6.6 cm
Sumbergh

   g) Shetland Isles (10 bonus points for this)
   h) Lerwick (30 bonus points for this)

Q3 all ans to nearest km where appropriate
   a) 025° 12 km
   b) 230° 5 km
   c) 320° 12 km
   d) 035° 19 km
   e) 165° 13 km
   f) 095° 28 km

Q4 215°

Q5 040°

Page 66

Q1 a) 3 m²
   b) 15 cm²
   c) 6 m²
   d) 17.82 cm²
   e) 7.2 m²
   f) 4.14 cm²
   g) 24.4 cm²
   h) 6.75 m²

Q2 a) 3 cm²
   b) 2 cm²
   c) 2.5 cm²

The Answers

d) 4 cm²
e) 2 cm²
f) 4 cm²
g) 3 cm²
h) 6 cm²

Q3 all triangles must have vertical height 6 cm

Q4 square 4 cm × 4 cm, other answers will vary

Q5 a) 936 cm²
b) 7.73 cm²
c) 255 mm²

Page 67

Q1 a) 5 units³
b) 12 units³
c) 7 units³

Q2 a) 60 cm³
b) 125 cm³
c) 36 ft³
d) 5.964 m³
e) 6440 cm³
f) 0.24 m³
g) 5 964 000 cm³; 240 000 cm³

Q3 fridge - 720 000 cm³
cereal - correct
juice - 1008.6 cm³
stock cube - 1 920 000 cm³

Page 68

Q1 a) 48 cm³
b) 2 cm
c) E.g. 2 × 2 × 12; 3 × 4 × 4;
1 × 6 × 4 (all measurements in cm)

Q2 a) 120 cm³
b) 960 cm³
c) 35

Q3 a) 11.25 cm³
b) 60 sweets (= 4 × 3 × 5)
c) 720 cm³
d) 45 cm³

Q4 a) volumes 30 cm³; 12 cm³; 200 cm³
b) areas 62 cm²; 40 cm²; 280 cm²
c) edges 40 cm; 40 cm; 128 cm

Section 6 — Handling Data

Page 69

Q1 a) 1: survey or observation
b) 2: experiment
c) 1: survey or observation
d) 3: secondary data
e) 1: survey or observation
f) 3: secondary data
g) 3: secondary data
h) 1: survey or observation

Q2 (i) Some test like catching a ruler or
something when you don't know when
it's going to be dropped.
(ii) Need to test a random sample of pupils.
(iii) A 'large enough' number of people —
at least 20 or so.
(iv) Make sure all ages and abilities are
represented in your sample.

Q3 (i) Things like: "What type of TV
programme do you like most?
a: drama b: comedy
c: current affairs d: sport" etc.
(ii) A wide selection of people from
different age groups, locations, social
groups etc.
(iii) Loads — the more the better.
For a national survey, you'd need at
least 1000.

Q4 Use random numbers to choose.
Could choose a random page, then a
random column, and a random entry from
that column.
Should realise problem of people
ex-directory or not on phone.
Method is cheap and easy.

Page 70

Q1 Pupils should allow for the whole price range.
Need enough bands to get enough detail.

Q2

Number of goals	0	1	2	3	4	5	6	7	8
Tally	I	III	ЖНІ II	II	II				I
Frequency	1	3	7	2	2	0	0	0	1

Q3 Pupils should allow for the very
small / tall, and have continuous groups so
that there are no 'gaps' between class
boundaries. There should be enough classes
so there's enough detail. Also, there should
be no confusion over group boundaries.

Q4 For example:

	0 - 9	10 - 19	20 - 29	30 - 39	40 - 49	50+
Cars per minute						
Tally						
Frequency						

a) Monday to Friday. Between 8 am and
9.30 am, and between 3 pm until 6 pm
would probably be most useful.
b) It would probably not be that useful, as the
school will probably be closed anyway.
c) It would probably show a lot of traffic
initially, before the school holidays.
Then when the school breaks up for its
summer holiday, traffic levels would
probably fall, as there will be less
school traffic. Then in early September,
traffic levels would probably increase
again as people go back to school.

Page 71

Q1

	Male	Female	Total
Junior	87	92	179
Senior	245	351	596
Total	332	443	775

a) 92
b) 443
c) 332
d) 596
e) 775
f)

	Male	Female	Total
Junior	87	94	181
Senior	246	351	597
Total	333	445	778

Q2

	Girl	Boy	Animal	Total
Walk	1	0	1	2
Bike / trike	1	2	1	4
Car	1	1	1	3
Bus / coach	2	3	2	7
Train	1	1	1	3
Total	6	7	6	19

Page 72

Q1 a) mode 5.5 kg; mean 5.4 kg
b) mode 229; mean 227.5
c) mode 8.1 m; mean 6.575 m
d) mode 0.2 and 0.6; mean 0.42

Q2 a) median 49; range 19
b) median 61g; range 49 g
c) median 55.5 cm; range 27 cm
d) median 1004.5; range 6

Q3 a) 172 cm
b) 64 cm
c) There are two — 167 cm and 176 cm.
d) New median = 171 cm, and new
range of 65 cm (mode not affected).

Page 73

Q1 a) 31
b) 33.5
c) 76
d) Probably not
e) Probably not

Q2 median 1.2 cm; range 4 cm

Q3 a) 10
b) 7
c) 28, 33
d) 88
e) 4, 1

Q4 For example: 5, 5, 5, 5, 5
and 4, 5, 5, 6
and 1, 3, 5, 5, 7, 9.

Q5 For example:
10, 12, 14, 16, 18, 20, 22, 24
(mean = 17, range = 14)
and 3, 8, 12, 16, 18, 22, 26, 31
(mean = 17, range = 28)

Page 74

Q1 a) Portugal
b) UK
c) Spain 5500 - 6000, Sweden 550-650,
UK 3500 - 4000 (these are
approximate, due to inaccuracies of
reading chart and rounding errors).

Q2

	Frequency	Angle
none	21	63
UK	48	144
Europe	29	87
North America	12	36
Asia	5	15
Other	5	15
total	120	360°

a)

The Answers

b)
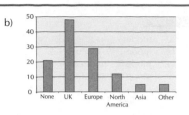

Page 75

Q1 a)

Year	Number of shell suits bought by shell suit owners	Number of 'first' shell suits bought	Total shell suits bought	Number of shell suits thrown out
1993	339	57	396	27
1994	357	65	422	40
1995	389	82	471	63
1996	360	125	485	129
1997	279	140	419	160
1998	257	137	394	175
1999	241	135	376	135
2000	192	130	322	168
2001	179	122	301	170

b)
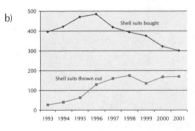

c) Overall, the number of shell suits being thrown out is increasing, while the number bought is decreasing.

Q2 a)
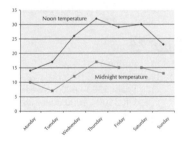

The midday temperatures rise in the middle of the week but start to fall.
b) The midnight temperatures rise in the middle of the week but also start to fall.
c) After a very wet start to the week, the rain stops between Tuesday and Saturday, but it then starts to rain again on Sunday.

Page 76

Q1 a) Mr Dingle: mean = 53.3, median = 59.5, range = 73
Ms Fangle: mean = 58.25, median = 55, range = 25
b) Ms Fangle — her figures have a smaller range (because Mr Dingle has some very high and very low figures for some months).
c) Mr Dingle should use the median, and Ms Fangle should use the mean.
d) Ms Fangle probably — she sold more holidays.

Q2 a) mode 20, median 27.5, mean 27, range 13 — mean or median probably best (mode at bottom of range and could be misleading).
b) mode 30, median 27.5, mean 24.25, range 21 — median probably best; mean affected by 1 small result.
c) mode £10, median £10, mean £3133.75, range £24990 — mode probably best; the one large prize has a dramatic effect on the mean.
d) mode £180, median £292.50, mean £357.63, range £809 — median probably best; mean affected by one large price; mode at bottom of range.

Q3 Duncan. More data needed before you can say whether the dice is biased — results evenly spread so far.

Page 77

Q1 a) certain (but not necessarily within the Arctic or Antarctic circles)
b) even chance
c) pupils' answers will vary
d) impossible
e) pupils' answers will vary
f) impossible (barring technological advances)
g) even chance
h) unlikely
i) likely (though pupils' answers may vary)
j) unlikely (for me, anyway)

Q2 a) Machine 1
b) Machine 2
c) Machine 1

Q3 Neither of them — each ball is equally likely (or unlikely) to be picked each week.

Page 78

Q1 a) 1/11
b) 2/11
c) 3/11
d) 4/11
e) 5/11
f) 5/11
g) 2/11
h) 2/11

Q2 a) 9/28
b) 6/28 = 3/14
c) 5/28
d) 20/28 = 5/7
e) 22/28

Q3 1/8

Q4 a) 1/50, 0.02, 2%
b) 49/50 (or 0.98 or 98%)

Page 79

Q1

	1	2	3	4	5	6
Head (H)	H1	H2	H3	H4	H5	H6
Tail (T)	T1	T2	T3	T4	T5	T6

a) 1/12
b) 1/12
c) 3/12 = 1/4
d) 3/12 = 1/4
e) 4/12 = 1/3
f) 2/12 = 1/6

g) 8/12 = 2/3
h) 0

Q2

+	0	2	4	6	8	10
1	1	3	5	7	9	11
3	3	5	7	9	11	13
5	5	7	9	11	13	15
7	7	9	11	13	15	17

a) 1/24
b) 3/24 = 1/8
c) 7 or 9 or 11
d) 10/24 = 5/12
e) 0

×	0	2	4	6	8	10
1	0	2	4	6	8	10
3	0	6	12	18	24	30
5	0	10	20	30	40	50
7	0	14	28	42	56	70

f) 1
g) 4/24 = 1/6
h) 9/24 = 3/8
i) 4/24 = 1/6

Page 80

Q1 a) 62/100 = 31/50
b) 79/200
c) about 395 tails and 605 heads

Q2 a) Portia's dice biased — frequencies should be roughly the same for all outcomes.
b) Juliet cheated — experimental probability is unlikely to equal the theoretical probability exactly.

Q3 Probably not — numbers close enough to assume lottery selection is unbiased, so you can assume that all numbers are equally likely to be picked.

Page 81

Q1 a) 2
b) 5 chocolates, 5 toffees, 6 mints
c) 5/16
d) 6/16 = 3/8
e) mint

Q2 E.g. roll 3 dice together 100 times, and count the number of times you get 3 even numbers. Divide that number by 100 to get an estimate of the probability.
EEE, EEO, EOE, EOO, OEE, OEO, OOE, OOO (E means an even number, O means an odd.) So theoretical probability = 1/8.

Q3 a) E.g. roll the dice, choose pork if dice shows 1 or 2, choose salad if dice shows 3 or 4, and choose fish if dice shows 5 or 6. Similarly for dessert.
b) PA, PY, PB, SA, SY, SB, FA, FY, FB
[P = Pork, S = Salad, F = Fish, A = Apple pie, Y = yoghurt, B = Banana]
c) 3/9 = 1/3
d) 1/9
e) 6/9 = 2/3
f) 18
g) Probably not.